INTRODUCING INSECTS
A BOOK FOR BEGINNERS

By JAMES G. NEEDHAM

Emeritus Professor of Entomology
in Cornell University

With Illustrations by
ELLEN EDMONSON

FIELD-CRICKETS

THE JAQUES CATTELL PRESS
LANCASTER, PENNSYLVANIA
1943

PRINTED IN THE UNITED STATES OF AMERICA
BY THE SCIENCE PRESS PRINTING COMPANY
LANCASTER, PENNSYLVANIA

PREFACE

This book is intended for people who want a little information about common insects, presented in language that any one can understand. Here is the information that most concerns an ordinary citizen, with all the technicalities left out. The insects are called by their common names. With the aid of good pictures, something is told of what they are like and where they are found and what they do in the world.

The way to control the pests among them is told in simple and practical terms, with stress upon the necessity of knowing their life history and habits. The vulnerable points in the life history are discovered in the search for such knowledge.

Then some aid is offered the beginner who wishes to know insects better and to enjoy something more of their beauty and infinite variety by doing a little collecting of them. Many a good naturalist has started his career by making a collection of insects. The concluding pages are intended for those beginners who may desire through their own collecting activities to reach the threshold of entomological science.

Acknowledgment is hereby made of figures borrowed from the publications of the United States Department of Agriculture to be found on pages 6, 9, 20, 22, 83 and 84, and from those of the Illinois State Laboratory of Natural History, on page 65. Others from the author's own *Natural History of the Farm* are found on pages 15, 44, 87 and 88, and from his *General Biology,* on pages 68 and 92.

CONTENTS

WHY STUDY INSECTS

When you bite into an apple, a fine, ripe, red, juicy apple, and take a big piece out of it, and find a worm in it, isn't it funny how suddenly you lose your liking for it!

If, instead of throwing the apple away, you take a good look at the worm, you will see that it is a soft, helpless, slow-moving, wriggling thing; and you may wonder how it got in there. How did it come to make its home in the

apple? That is something worth finding out; for if you knew that, you might know how to keep worms out of apples. To an apple grower that is very important, and to an apple-eater it should be interesting.

The adult insect is the Codling Moth. It is well known as a destroyer of apples the world around. The adult moth is a pretty little brownish gray insect with a wingspread of about three quarters of an inch. It may be recognized among other gray moths of about the same size by coppery bronze markings about the outer margins of the fore wings.

The story of the Codling Moth may be very briefly told

as follows: When the bloom of the orchard is passing in spring, and the last of the petals are falling from the apple blossoms, and the little, fuzzy green fruits, smaller than peas, are still crowned with the withered stamens of the faded flowers, then you may expect that the codling moths will soon be flitting about among the branches of the apple trees, seeking a place to lay their eggs. They are hunting for the little apples. The mother moth will lay her eggs,

one in a place, on the side of little apples, or on a leaf nearby. She will stick them fast to the fuzzy skin, and leave them there to hatch.

At this time the apples stand upright on the stems. When the little caterpillar comes out from the egg shell, it generally crawls upward seeking a hiding place, and creeps into the "eye" of the apple between the bases of the stamens. There it begins to dig in. It eats its way downward toward the core of the apple until it is safe and snug inside.

When the caterpillar has lived in the apple for about a month and has grown to full size it leaves the fruit and creeps down the trunk of the tree into a crevice under the bark or some other such sheltered place, and spins about itself a thin cocoon of silk. In this it remains for two weeks or more in hiding. Then it comes out as an adult codling moth; and soon it will be ready to lay eggs again for another brood.

Now, what can you do to keep the codling moth from making your apples "wormy"?

It has been found that the caterpillar is easily killed with lead arsenate, added to its food, and that this poison may be sprayed all over the tree, mixed with water, or blown over its foliage as dust. But, clearly, the only time its food can be reached with the poison is the time of its first meal before it has gone inside the apple. Therefore, put on the poison when the last of the petals are falling to catch the first brood of worms, and again about the last week in July to catch the second brood.

The land is so well stocked with codling moths—so many neglected orchards are serving as hatcheries for them—that you can't raise the highest grade of worm-free apples without fighting the worms.

So you see, if you ever raise apples, you will need to know the times and seasons of the Codling Moth: where it is staying and what it is doing all the season through.

And on the use you make of this knowledge will depend whether your apple crop will

look like this

or like this

When you open your wardrobe to get out your woolens and furs for cold weather, if you find them eaten full of holes and falling to pieces, there isn't anything you can do about it. It is too late. The clothes moths have got them; and somebody will have to dig up money for new ones.

THE MOTHS "GOT" THIS ONE —→

But this need not happen. If you know the ways of the clothes moths, you can avoid such losses by keeping your furs in cold storage; or if you will take a little trouble and use a little foresight you can keep them safely at home, by observing the simple precautions described on page eighty-two.

[5]

If in climbing the stairs at home, you should feel a step giving way, you might blame the carpenter who built the house. But the stairs may have been strongly built by the carpenter, and later made weak by another wood-worker of a very different sort; for there is an insect called a termite that eats wood, even stair supports. Termites may enter your house unseen by gnawing their way through solid timbers. So, they may hollow out the beams that support your stairway, leaving only a thin shell of wood that will crumple under your weight.

Termites are pale, yellowish, soft-bodied, strong-jawed insects of the form shown in the picture. They shun the light of day. You will never see them out in the open. They live in nests, many together, and make covered runways out from the nests to places where they can find

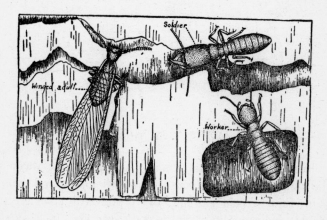

food. They eat wood—just plain, dry wood. They like to make their nests about the foundation of houses, with passageways up into the timbers above. They work slowly, but great numbers of them working together make long tunnels through the wood, leaving it weakened and hollow. They may go up into floors, and on up into furniture if wooden parts rest directly on the floors. They may get into the legs of your table and eat them hollow, so that the table will fall of its own weight. When they get into bookcases, they may eat the paper between the covers of the books; for that, if made of wood fibre, also suits their taste. In such ways as this they do great damage in houses and in libraries.

Termites are very common in the South, and they seem to be spreading northward in recent years. Damage is now frequently reported as far north as the Great Lakes.

It is easy to avoid this injury by a little forethought. Termites travel afoot and under cover, and they eat only wood. If, therefore, in building a house, the sills and other parts next the foundation are covered with tar or some other good repellent, the termites will not enter. They refuse to bite into the tar.

When, however, they are already established in a house, a cure must be found. First find their nest. Then find some way of putting a poison in it. Make a hole into the covered interior and put in the poison. If this is carbon bisulphide, it may be poured in through a tube; if calcium cyanide dust, it may be thrown or blown in.

Poisons do their work quickly; but they are all dangerous; and when you use them you must follow carefully the safety precautions that are printed on the packages in which they are sold.

When your dog scratches himself, something is biting him—probably fleas. Lift the long hair on his back and look under it quickly, and if you can see a little, thin, brown insect slipping away instantly among the hairs, then, you *know* he has fleas. They make him uncomfortable. They bite him; and, so, he scratches to make them quit. But about all he can do is to make them move along; and soon they are biting him again in a new place.

Now, if you want to do something for his comfort, give him a bath of creolin. Put enough warm water in a tub to cover his body lying down. Add four tablespoons of creolin for each gallon of water. Stir well. Fold up his legs and lay him down in the bath. Brush his hair the wrong way to lift it and to let the bath water under it to wet his skin thoroughly, and keep him there for several minutes.

You can't put his head under, because the creolin would

[8]

hurt his eyes and nose. But the hair on his head is so short that you can see any fleas that may run up there to avoid the wet, and you can comb them into the bath. Then wash him with soap and warm water to remove the creolin.

So, you may kill the fleas; and you will see at once that he sleeps better, looks better, stops scratching, leaves less loose hair around the place, and is altogether a more respectable dog.

There may be fleas in his bedding; and if you don't clean that up too, he may at once pick up a new supply of them. Sprinkle flake naphthalene thickly in his bed and leave it there.

These are just a few of the ways in which insects do us injury. There are many others. These show how important it is that we should know something about insects in order to be able to control the harmful ones.

But there is another side to the picture of our relations with insects. Let us now look at that. There are useful insects as well as injurious ones. The bees that hum among the apple blossoms are carrying pollen from flower to flower. They thus make possible the fertilization of the flowers and the setting of the fruit. Without this work that the willing bees do for us there could be no apple crop. Without bees we would have no honey. Without silk worms we would have no real silks.

When on some fine day you go out into the meadow where there are flowers freshly blooming, you will be sure to see some beautifully colored butterflies and beetles about the flowers. Added to the fragrance of the flowers and the glory of the sunshine will be the touch of beauty and grace in action that these insects add to the flower garden.

You will see the butterflies alighting daintily upon the blossoms, and sucking nectar out of their depths for food. They start away suddenly if you come too near, but if you approach cautiously you may see one unroll its long coiled tubular tongue and put the tip of it into the throat of an open flower, reaching down to the nectaries in the bottom. And when you get near enough the butterfly before you may be like one of the exquisite creatures shown here.

You will see that the beetles are clambering rather roughly about over the flower clusters, eating their yellow pollen from the anthers of the flowers. They are very different from the butterflies in both form and action. The beetles are rough-and-tumble fellows, sturdily built, with hard shells and strong claws for hanging on and climbing. Their beauty is of a different kind: beauty of form and color as before, but none of the daintiness of the butterflies either in structure or in action.

You find that both butterflies and beetles while feeding themselves are doing a very important work for the flowers. They are carrying pollen from one flower to another, making cross-fertilization possible, and enabling the plants to set seed. The butterflies work with great precision as they carry pollen on their beaks and deposit it directly on the stigmas of the next flowers visited. The lumbering beetles merely get well besprinkled with pollen

SOME COMMON BUTTERFLIES

THE
MOURNING CLOAK

THE GRAY
HAIR-STREAK

THE
VICEROY

THE
SILVER-SPOTTED
SKIPPER

THE
MONARCH

THE
AMERICAN
COPPER

THE
TIGER
SWALLOW-TAIL

THE
RED ADMIRAL

on all their underparts while lolling on a flower cluster, and then they broadcast it, so to speak, over the entire cluster that is next visited.

When you have seen these things you will surely want to get a closer look at the insects themselves. The best way to get it is to capture and preserve a few fine specimens for later study indoors. In the long evenings of winter they will be pleasant reminders of hours spent amid scenes of natural interest and beauty in the summer season. Then they may become the basis of further studies of insects made with the aid of books. Butterflies and beetles have always been the collectors' favorite insects, and in almost any library there will be found books about them.

As you are walking through the meadow, other insects will rise before your feet in flight. Off they will go with a great showing of wings, and then, suddenly settling, they will absolutely disappear from view; and you will look for them in vain until they arise again in flight. Why can't you see them sitting? It is because they are colored in such a way as to be invisible. They settle where their colors match the background. If they are gray-streaked moths, they settle among the dry grass leaves; if they are plain, green leaf-hoppers or meadow grasshoppers, they settle among the green leaves. If they are gray roadside grasshoppers, their backs all "pepper-and-salt colored," they settle in the dust. When you get them in your insect net you can see them there well enough; so sweep the grass with your net and catch them in it, and when you have them before you, then look for resemblances to grass stems (streakings in green and browns), to dead leaves (patterns in browns), and to bark (patterns in gray) in their coloration.   Nature has hidden them well.

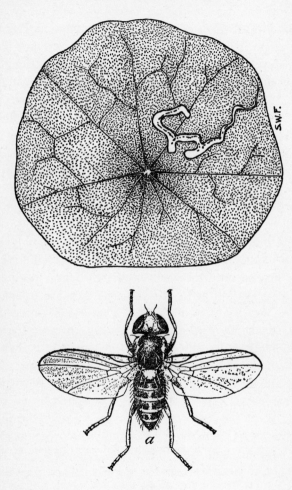

a

While you are out in the meadow look for some of the interesting homes that leaf-inhabiting insects make for themselves there. You can find leaves that have been neatly rolled like a scroll and fastened with white silken threads, with caterpillars living inside. You can find leaves folded flat, leaves sewed together, leaves tied in bunches; all fastened with threads of silk and with different kinds of caterpillars living in them. You can even find leaves that have a minute cavern dug out of their interior —a "leaf mine"—with some of the smallest of caterpillars living inside. A nasturtium leaf-mine is shown here, and below it, the fly that develops in it. You can find stems that are bored out hollow for a dwelling place, and nuts and fruits likewise. A naturalist of long ago, Rev. J. G. Wood, once wrote a book on this most interesting subject, and called it *Homes without Hands*.

When you are passing under the low bough of a basswood tree at the edge of the woods, if you will overturn one of its broad leaves and look carefully at its under side you may see a whole flock of dainty little lace-bugs, like the one shown here, clinging to it; all with their beaks

inserted into the tissues of the leaf, sucking out its sap. Wonderful little creatures they are, in all this microscopic finery, which is their every-day apparel. The basswood tree is their home. And there you see another thing that is common in the insect world: there are many insects that live on a single kind of plant, and that are found in constant association with it.

[14]

Then walk to the edge of a pond or a pool and look down into the clear still water and see the water beetles swimming about. You will see that, whether they are big or little, they are all of one shape—pointed toward the

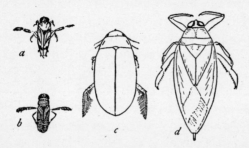

ends and smoothly rounded off—that is, *boat shaped*. And they are all furnished with long, flat, oar-like hind legs for swimming. At *a* is shown a back-swimmer (it swims habitually up-side-down); at *b,* a water boatman; at *c,* a diving beetle (another large one is shown below on the page); and at *d,* a giant water-bug. How fit they are for life in the water! And wherever you look for insects you will find this same wonderful fitness to place and manner of life. It is one of Nature's most useful lessons.

So you may learn from insects much that is of interest and educational value, if only you have the eyes to see.

The world is full of insects. There are more kinds of insects than of all the other animals put together. Many are beautiful. All are interesting when you know enough about them. One, the honeybee, is sheltered and cared for as domesticated animal. A few others produce vauable products. A few are harmful.

When we think of the many ways in which they may do us injury these do not seem to be so few. They eat our growing crops. They eat our stored foods: cereals, roots, fruits, nuts, meats, everything that we eat. They like the things we use. They eat our woolen clothes, rugs and furs. They suck the blood of our livestock and pets. They even get on our persons and bite us; and, worst of all, in so doing they carry from person to person the germs of infectious diseases. But others among them are busy distributors of pollen in our flower gardens, insuring crops of seeds, and they are themselves the principal food of many birds and other useful animals. Since they affect our welfare in so many ways, we ought to know something about them.

HOW TO STUDY INSECTS

An old familiar recipe for cooking a rabbit begins: "First catch the rabbit." So in this study, the first thing to do is to catch the insects. Lay hands on them; get them where you can see them well. Fortunately, the equipment needed is simpler and less expensive than are guns and rabbit traps. You will find it described on pages one hundred and seven to one hundred and nine.

Two things are needed at the start: a net for capturing and a cyanide bottle for quickly killing the insects. And then a third thing needed is a little action on your own part. So get these two tools of the bug-hunter's trade and get busy with them. Learn how to use the net; how to swing it with precision; how to keep the agile insect captive inside by a quick turn of the wrist, making a fold in the net bottom; how to insert the cyanide bottle, and get the captive securely in it.

Go collecting. At first, go wherever you like, and collect whatever insects you see. Collect from the flowers of the meadow or lawn. Collect by sweeping the grass. Collect by the pondside or streamside. Collect at night the swarming insects that are attracted to bright lights.

You will soon learn that some insects are easy to catch and some are exceedingly difficult. Get all kinds; and in the getting of them note where they live and how they

[17]

behave. See how wonderfully different they are; big and little; hard-shelled and soft; quick and slow; showy and hard-to-see; quickly overcome by cyanide fumes, or slowly succumbing. Note how their flight varies in swiftness and steadiness, and height. Note where they alight and how they stand, or walk, or run, or hide. And, using the figures of this book, learn the names of some of them.

Thus you will begin to know insects, and you will be ready later to collect the particular things that are discussed in the chapters that follow. If you would really know these things, collect and study them, and do not be content with merely reading about them.

In the following pages there are some lessons on common and important and interesting insects. Each indoor study is best prepared for by a little collecting. By using your net and your eyes diligently, you will learn how and where the insects live, and what they do in the world. The specimens collected are to be compared with the figures and descriptions given in the lessons. Thus you may learn how to recognize them and become able to speak of them intelligently.

On pages one hundred and two to one hundred and five you will find some information as to methods of control of harmful insects; and on pages one hundred and six to one hundred and thirteen there are some instructions for collection making and for the preservation of specimens.

BUTTERFLIES

On some fine, sunshiny day in warm weather, take a net in hand and go out after butterflies. Take also a cyanide bottle (see page eighty-nine) of large size; for you may need space to hold a mourning-cloak, or one of the big swallow-tails. What you may find will depend on place and season; what you may catch will depend on your skill in the use of the net.

The smaller butterflies that are commoner are easy to catch. First visit a garden where there are cabbages growing and see if there are not some white cabbage butterflies in the air above it. These when young (larvae or caterpillars) feed upon cabbage

leaves and are often called "cabbage worms." Possibly you may see a female butterfly, settled upon a cabbage leaf, laying her eggs there. The eggs are pale specks, smaller than a pinhead, shaped like an inverted teacup with ribbed sides.

In almost any cabbage patch that is not very well kept, leaves that are raggedly eaten in holes will betray the presence of the caterpillars. Their soft green color exactly matches that of the leaf, and protects them from being seen; but sharp eyes will find them, either at the leaf edges, feeding, or in some hollow of the leaf resting upon a thin-spun mattress of white silk.

These worm-like slow-moving, green caterpillars are surely very different from the winged butterflies. Their change into butterflies is a wonderful thing. The "worm" when full grown stops eating and usually crawls away from the green cabbage to some fence or tree trunk. Finding a suitable ledge, generally a foot or more above the ground, it spins a layer of silk and fastens its tail end to the silk. Then it spins a semi-circular loop of silk about the middle of its body, and sheds its skin. Out of the old crumpling skin comes a pale chrysalis or pupa, of

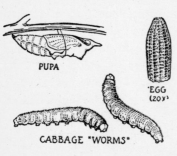

PUPA

'EGG (20 Y)

CABBAGE "WORMS"

the form shown in our figure. At first it is pale green, but it soon dries to a neutral tint that better matches its new surroundings. The parts of the butterfly are already marked out upon the surface of the chrysalis, but

[20]

they are not yet free; the only moving it can do is a twisting of the rear end of the body. But while it is quiet, a butterfly is being formed within its shell; and at the end of the resting stage the shell will burst and a butterfly will come out of it.

If you will search the stakes and fences about the borders of the cabbage patch, you may find some of these chrysalids; and if you will remove them carefully and take them home and put them in a covered glass jar, in a short time the butterflies will come out of them. You should have in the jar an inch-wide strip of wire cloth, bent in L-shape and resting on the bottom and against the glass on one side of the jar, to serve as a ladder up which the butterflies may climb; for they cannot cling to the bare glass.

Occasionally a crop of little parasites that have fed on the caterpillar will come out instead of butterflies. Even so, their rearing will be worth while, for these parasites will show you one of Nature's aids to the gardener in control of cabbage worms.

If no chrysalids can be found, they may be easily obtained by rearing some of the larger cabbage-worms. You have only to put grown caterpillars into a jar, with fresh pieces of cabbage leaves for them to eat, and put on a lid. If they do not change in twenty-four hours, clean the glass and put in some fresh leaves with them, and let them alone for another day. Being unable to get farther away, they will usually do their spinning on the under side of the lid, where you may see how it is done.

This experiment will be still more worthwhile if you take time to observe the manner of the caterpillar's feed-

[21]

ing; for this will give the clue to proper means of control.

JAWS OF A CUTWORM

At the front end of the caterpillar is a little brown head bearing a cluster of minute eyes and a stubby feeler (antenna) on each side, and a mouth below. Under the broad lip that covers the mouth two pairs of minute jaws may be seen swinging from side to side, digging little chunks out of the cabbage leaf. The leaf is eaten bodily; so, all that is necessary to kill the "worms" is to put some poison on the leaves for them to eat (see page one hundred and three). On cabbages you must use a poison that will kill the insects but not the people who may later eat the cabbages. Such a poison is powdered hellebore; and it may be dusted on the cabbage leaves by hand, out of a pepper box.

When you have found the *egg,* the caterpillar or *larva,* the chrysalis or *pupa,* and the *adult* butterfly, then you will have seen the four stages that make up the full life history of this insect. Most insects pass through these same four stages in the course of their development, but see also page one hundred and twelve. It is in the larval stage that most of the damage is done by the injurious species.

The most injurious butterfly in the world is this one

SOUTHERN CABBAGE BUTTERFLY

POTHERB BUTTERFLY

[22]

that haunts the cabbage patches. It is an immigrant from Europe. Some of its native American relatives are shown in the accompanying figure. All these feed as larvae on plants of the cabbage family, which includes cresses and mustards.

It is the caterpillars of moths and not of butterflies that are most harmful. These will be discussed in the chapter beginning on page forty-four.

If you will next visit a field of blossoming red clover, you may expect to find some of the smaller yellow, or sulfur butterflies there. The caterpillars feed on clover. Also, the butterflies themselves sip the nectar of the clover blossoms. One may often be seen sitting on the top of a clover head probing the deep, tubular flowers, one by one, with its long sucking tongue, or proboscis.

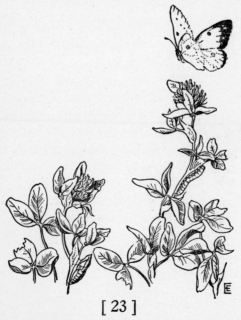

These caterpillars are not so easy to find as are cabbage worms, which they much resemble. They are best obtained by sweeping the tops of the clover with an insect net. The net will find them where none can be seen with the eye.

If the weather be hot and dry and the roads dusty, wherever there is a roadside pool, as at the overflow from a watering trough, you may find large numbers of these and other butterflies gathered together. They will be sitting on the mud, quenching their thirst. Here, by approaching cautiously so as not to startle them, you may see how they unroll the long, coiled "tongue" through which they take their liquid food, and how they thrust its tip down into the mud where the water is.

THE ROADSIDE BUTTERFLY   MALE

You can catch a lot of them quickly in such a place. A rather slow sweep of the net just above the ground will gather them in as they arise in flight. Among the sulfurs of the roadside may be several of the forms shown in our figure: One with a sketchy picture of a dog's head on each fore wing (4); the roadside clover sulfur just described, and the little sulfur. And drinking with them will be other butterflies, like some of those shown in the figure on page nine.

THE LITTLE SULFUR

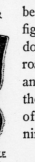
THE DOG'S-HEAD   MALE

Thistles and asters and button-bush and most other showy flowers attract

[24]

butterflies in great variety. One of our milkweeds is so attractive to them in its season that it is called the butterfly weed. Along the blossoming roadside or edge of the wood you will find them in great variety. There will be big swallow-tails, little coppers, and hair-streaks, the familiar red-brown monarch and the viceroy, grotesque angle-wings, among which the over-wintering mourning cloak is the most familiar, richly variegated admirals, little brown skippers, and all the rest—a wonderful lot of the most beautiful of living things.

DRAGONFLIES

When you go out to a pond for dragonflies, take a cyanide bottle of the largest size; for some of the big green darners may be about, and if you are nimble enough and lucky enough you may catch one. Collecting will be better if the day is warm and sunshiny, for the pond-loving dragonflies delight in sunshine. As you approach the water some of the large ones may be seen circling about on horizontally outspread wings over its shining surface. No other insects fly so steadily, or keep so closely to one level in their dartings about.

Swift they are, too, and artful at dodging a net, as you soon learn when you try to capture the larger ones. It is useless to run after them; you can only get them when they fly within easy reach of your net. So you must use strategy. If you watch their coming and going carefully, you will soon see that there are points on the shore that they pass and repass as though flying on a regular beat. So, quietly station yourself at one of these points and wait for them to pass. Soon you will learn that they dodge the net best when they meet its stroke head on, and are more easily taken when the net is brought up from behind them. And when you have learned to take a proper station, to keep still, to wait and watch for them to come within reach, to keep the net down out of sight until they are opposite you, and then to bring it up swiftly and take them by a stroke from the rear, then you may begin to collect the big dragonflies successfully.

If they are too quick for you and you can't catch any of them in flight, then try a stroke at one sitting on a reed tip in the open. You will have to approach it very cautiously until it is within reach of the net. And you should hold the net still and keep it well out of sight until ready for the stroke. Then a swift stroke from the rear should be followed by a very lively rustling of wings in your net bag. You will soon learn by experience how quickly your captive dragonfly may slip out of the bag and fly skyward if given the slightest chance. A quick turn of the wrist at the end of the stroke will fold the net, and

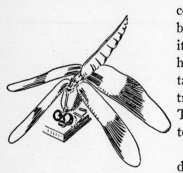

confine the dragonfly in the bottom of its bag; and since it is quite harmless your hand may be put inside to take it by the wings for transfer to the killing bottle. Then you have something to study.

Many pond-inhabiting dragonflies perch in the open

upon reed tips, others on logs and stones on the ground. The common white-tail shown in our figure often settles itself on light-colored surfaces of boards or bare earth, adjusting its wings in this forward-drooping position by a succession of jerks (see p. twenty-seven).

Among the larger pond-inhabiting dragonflies there are some that are easily known by the conspicuous color pattern of their wings. Four of these wing patterns are shown in our figures: there is the Widow, for example; she wears mourning bands of crepe-like, dull black color across the bases of the four wings: and there is the Ten Spot with a dozen patches of brown arranged as shown in our figure of a young one. When older there appear the ten spots of chalky whiteness that give the common name, two on each fore wing, and three on each hind wing. This whitening of certain parts is the hoariness of age in

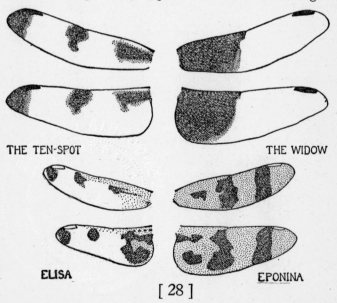

THE TEN-SPOT   THE WIDOW

ELISA   EPONINA

[28]

47430

dragonflies. Two pretty pond species of smaller stature and less robust form bear the names Elisa and Eponina: the spots shown in the wings of both are brown, but the wing membrane is clear as glass in Elisa, and golden yellow in Eponina.

The Raggedy Saddleback (shown on p. twenty-six both at rest and in flight) has the blackish band across the base of the hind wings jagged on its edges. This dragonfly is a superb flier, continuing on the wing nearly all day long, seeming never to rest nor ever to tire. Again and again it will hover before you tantalizingly, just beyond the reach of your net. It seems to know what is a safe distance. You will do well to catch one.

All the above-mentioned dragonflies stand hovering in mid-air between their dartings from place to place. There are other dragonflies about the pond that have very different habits of flight. Larger than any of the foregoing are the big Blue and Green Darners that go dashing about the neighborhood on broad transparent wings.

At the pond you may expect also some of the lesser members of this group that are commonly known as damsel-flies. These will be seen perching on the leaves that float on the surface, or flying so low that it will be difficult taking them in the net without dipping water. These rest with their transparent wings lifted above the back, and not spread out flatwise.

A DAMSEL-FLY

Some of them have bodies of metallic tints; some are striped at the front and ringed at the rear with bright blue and black; and a few of them are red.

[29]

Among the hovering dragonflies you may now and then see one that is making short dashes downward, touching the end of the body repeatedly to the surface of water, and rising again after each dip. This is a female engaged in laying her eggs. She drops them in the water, perhaps a dozen of them at every descent, for they are very numerous. They at once settle to the bottom, and being very minute, are quite undiscoverable among the bottom sediment. If a female skimmer can be captured in the act, her eggs may be obtained in this way: take her by the tips of the fore wings held closed together between the thumb and finger of one hand (leaving the hind wings free to flap), swing her up and down, imitating her own natural flying movements, touching the tip of the tail at each descent to the surface of the water in a full glass tumbler held in the other hand; she will generally liberate some eggs there where they can be seen.

These eggs hatch into little sprawling creatures that are very different in form and appearance from the adult dragonflies, but with similar insect-eating habits. They

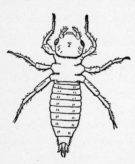

live in the water for a year or more; and when they are grown they clamber up some stem or post or bank above the water level and transform into such dragonflies as we see flying. We may learn what they are like without going into the water after them, by merely observing the form in which they come out of it (see the figure on p. twenty-six) ; each one bears a thick gray skin, something like a coat of mail; and when the winged dragonfly comes out of it through a rent in its back, this skin is left hanging attached by its claws in the place to which it climbed. So now, while you are at the pond, the skins of some of these dragonflies, that are darting about over the pond, may, with a little searching, be found sticking to solid supports of any kind a few inches above the surface of the water, empty and brittle and dry.

You may also, perhaps, observe the dragonflies feeding, though this is harder to see. They eat other insects. They capture their prey in flight, but many of them sit down to eat, especially if it is their "big game" that they have captured. Some may be seen perching on weed-tips beside a path, or even on the bare earth, and if you approach them cautiously so as not to scare them, you may perhaps see a fly or a mosquito chewed up and swallowed. Oftener, however, you will find the remains of a meal half-eaten in the bottom of your net after a successful stroke at a perching dragonfly.

Much of the darting about over the pond is not aimless, but is directed toward the capture of little flies, midges, and mosquitos that hover there in the air. As mosquito-eaters the dragonflies are to be counted as friends and benefactors.

If you will take a good look at the first dragonflies captured there will be no excuse for confusing dragon-flies thereafter with other insects. The wobbly head almost overspread by the great compound eyes, the minute bristle-like feelers or antennae, the four big veiny wings, each with a hinge-like notch in the middle of its front border, and the long spiny legs, bunched together at the front of the body—these mark dragonflies unmistakably.

GRASSHOPPERS AND CRICKETS

Now, for a few grasshoppers! There are long horns and short horns among them. Some that prefer to live on or near the ground are short-horned grasshoppers; they

A SHORT-HORNED GRASSHOPPER

have antennae shorter than the body. They sit by your path in the meadow or garden, and spring into the air on your approach. They may alight again at once, or they may spread their wings and keep on going for a distance. If you can clap a net over one before it arises from the ground, it will generally spring up into the bag, where easily taken. The larger and more sluggish ones may be picked up with the fingers, if approached very slowly and then seized very quickly. Watch a young turkey "sneak up on" a grasshopper if you want to learn how to do it.

The Carolina grasshopper is one of the larger and handsomer species. It prefers the most open places, and sits commonly in the dust of the roadside. It "sits tight," waiting until it is almost stepped upon. Then it rises with a leap, and spreads its rustling wings, and goes fluttering along, with the black borders to its yellow hind wings showing conspicuously. Then it suddenly drops on the dust again, and vanishes absolutely from view. With its wings closed its colors match the dust of the road, and it has become invisible. Only by keeping an eye fixed on it when it settles can you follow it to its resting place.

The males of this species fly for the fun of it on hot afternoons, making grasshopper-music as they go, quite as described in James Whitcomb Riley's poem, *The South Wind and the Sun,* in these lines:

> Where the dusty highway leads,
> High above the wayside weeds
>
> . . . .
> The dull grasshopper sprung
> Half a man's height up, and hung
> Tranced in heat, with whirring wings,
> And sung, and sung, and sung.

One of the commonest of our species is the small red-legged grasshopper. It is about an inch long, and the spiny shanks of its long hind legs are red. The most famous of all our species is the Rocky Mountain grasshopper, that was a devastating scourge in Kansas and Nebraska in pioneer days.

The work of grasshoppers may be seen by the wayside, in weeds eaten full of holes, and in the ragged edges of the leaves of the corn and of grasses in the fields. You may observe their feeding habits in the field by taking

[33]

time to make a very careful approach, so as not to disturb them at their feeding; but you may see it much better by taking some of them home alive, keeping them in a cage (see p. one hundred and fourteen), and adding from time to time fresh food. Green clover or grass leaves suit their tastes. The use of the front feet in holding the food, and of the little palps or food feelers below the mouth in examining it, and of the jaws in cutting or tearing it, can thus be readily observed.

Incidentally, a grasshopper may be seen preening itself, washing its face like a cat with its front feet, cleaning its antenna by drawing it under a foot firmly planted on top, cleaning its hind feet by rubbing them together and its middle feet by licking them with the head bent far under the body, or polishing the braided surface of its big hind thighs by rubbing the bent knees of the middle legs against them. It is a model of personal cleanliness.

A live grasshopper may well be used for getting an understanding of the way in which an insect breathes. Put one in a cyanide bottle, and as soon as it falls over, stupefied, take it out and lay it on its side, and watch the breathing movements of the under side of its body. Observe that the long fold that extends backward from the base of the hind legs expands and contracts, bellows-like, at every breath.

Then note just above the fold on each ring of the body a little spiracle or breathing pore; and find another pore on the side of the body just above the base of the middle leg. An insect does not breathe through its mouth, but through these pores. These open into a complicated system of air tubes whose branches run through all the tissues of the body, supplying them air. This is the method of breathing in all insects, and, as we shall see later, is important to be kept in mind when considering methods of their control. Practically all of our insect poisons affect either feeding or respiration.

The short-horned grasshoppers, when abundant enough to be serious pests, are controlled by food poisons. Advantage is taken of their greedy appetite for grain and sweets, and a poisoned bait is prepared by mixing together attractive foods and poisons such as the following: wheat bran, 25 pounds; Paris green or white arsenic one pound; six finely chopped oranges; low grade molasses, two quarts; water, two to four gallons. The bran and the poison are mixed dry. The oranges are squeezed into the water, and then the syrup is added to it. Then all are mixed together thoroughly. The bait is sown broadcast into the infested fields, preferably in the early morning. Five to seven pounds to the acre is the rule. The grasshoppers eat this, preferring it, like candy, to their natural, less tasty food. They eat it and die.

The short-horned grasshoppers lay their eggs in the ground. The female digs a hole in the soil, using for the purpose four horny, pointed blades (which together form an ovipositor) at the tip of the end of her body. Holding the points close together, she pushes them into the soil, and then spreads them apart to widen the hole. Then she repeats the process until the hole is as deep as she can reach. Then she lays her eggs in the hole, and smears them over with a protective covering which hardens, forming the so-called "egg-pod." The whole process takes some time; and often at the proper season a female grass-

[35]

hopper may be seen on the bare earth beside a path, industriously probing with her down-turned tail-spikes, making the hole.

The long-horned grasshoppers commonly live among the foliage of shrubs and trees. These are mainly the meadow grasshoppers and katy-dids. They are generally greenish in color, matching their leafy background. They are not easy to see. You find them best by sweeping the tall weeds, or the garden bushes, or the roadside shrubbery, with a heavy beating net. Or, if you have good ears and a sense of direction, you may follow single individuals to their places of hiding by sound. The males of many species sing. *"Katy-did, Katy-did, Katy-did"* is the most familiar of their songs; but each species sings or chirps, in its own way, and each is recognizable by a trained ear. Indeed, professional collectors find the rarer species by tracing individuals by ear, following up the nocturnal songsters with a flashlight until found. But if you will seek out moist low-ground meadow and sweep the taller vegetation around the borders of it, you will find plenty of them. The antennae of all of them are very long

A
LONG-HORNED
GRASSHOPPER

and slender. Some of them with long, pointed foreheads are called cone-head grasshoppers.

It is only the males that sing. Their "singing" is more like fiddling; for the sound is produced by rubbing together the front wings, on the base of which there is a cross-ribbed vein at the edge of an expanded "sounding-board" area. The "ears" are located in the front legs. If you will look just below the knee you will see there a little swelling with a tympanum-like membrane stretched across a hollow in one side of it.

The females are similar in form, but are armed with a long, flat-bladed ovipositor instead of the tail spikes at the end of the body. This is used for inserting the eggs into deep protected places, as under the bases of scales and of leaves. The wings of the female are narrow at the base, lacking the musical apparatus of the male.

Crickets. Nearly allied to the grasshoppers, and similar

FIELD-CRICKETS

in habits and in jumping powers are the crickets. Their musical apparatus is much more elaborate, the sounding-board area of the fore wings of the male being expanded to cover the greater part of the wing. There are two familiar groups of these: blackish field crickets that live on the ground, and greenish tree crickets that live in the foliage.

The field crickets sun themselves in the paths of the meadow, and run to cover when scared. When you try to catch them you discover that although they jump well, they escape you best by slipping through the tangled fallen stems and leaves and grasses. The smooth finish of their dusky coats greatly favors this; they are "slippery." The "cricket on the hearth" was of this type—warmth-loving, crevice-haunting, familiar to the peasants of the Old World, whose hearthside was much more accessible to crickets than ours is.

The female of the field crickets has a very long, slender, cylindrical, sharp-pointed ovipositor by means of which

she places her eggs singly, deep in the soil. These crickets, if kept in a live cage (see page one hundred and fourteen), may be fed on prunes or other dried fruit.

The tree-crickets are more slender and delicate insects, with gauzy, greenish wings. They live in the low shrubbery, and in the trees. In autumn they fill the night air with their incessant chirpings. They chirp in unison; and that will at once distinguish their music from that of the katy-dids and others

SNOWY TREE-CRICKET just described. They begin in the

afternoon and chirp all night. At the very opening of their daily concert there may be some irregularity, but each performer soon catches the beat, and thereafter keeps perfect time to the end of his part in the monotonous performance.

The harm done by tree crickets is mainly that of the female in laying her eggs. Her ovipositor contains a pair of sharp cutting blades, and with these she cuts deep holes through the woody walls of pithy stems, such as those of the raspberry, and deposits her eggs in the pith. These are placed in neat rows; and they remain unchanged over winter, to hatch in the spring. Since the portion of the stem above the injury dies without producing a crop of berries the damage may be serious when the tree-crickets are very abundant. It is controlled by cutting out and burning the infested canes before the eggs hatch.

There is another group of crickets that live in the ground. These are burrowers and are known as mole crickets. They inhabit mainly the warmer parts of the country, and are found only locally, in moist, light or sandy soils, through which they dig by means of their broad, shovel-like front legs. They are seldom seen except when overturned with the soil, or when they are attracted to lights at night. They feed upon the tender roots of a variety of plants, and are sometimes a pest in southern gardens.

The young of all grasshoppers and crickets resemble the adult in form. They are not worm-like, as are caterpillars, but have long legs and antennae. They differ most from the adults by lack of developed wings (see figure on page one hundred and twenty-three). Between the actively feeding young and the adult there is no intervening pupal stage.

The young live in the same places as the adults and eat the same kinds of food. They chew it with the same kinds of jaws—little brown-tipped, toothed mandibles. Individually these seem small and insignificant, but the collective work of vast numbers of them once led the Hebrew prophet Joel to compare them to "the cheek-teeth of the great lion" in that entomological first chapter of his book in the *Bible*.

LEAF BUGS AND LEAF HOPPERS

If you will step out of doors anywhere and sweep the green herbage a few strokes with your net you will be sure to capture in it some rather small insects of the form shown in the next figure: flat-backed leaf bugs, and cylindric, quick-jumping leaf-hoppers. Young and adult stages may often be taken together. The adults fly readily; indeed, they are likely to escape you if you open the net incautiously.

These are important meadow and garden insects that feed upon the sap of plants. They do not chew the leaves, but puncture them and suck out the plant juices. Instead of biting jaws, they have a sharp beak that consists of four slender, sharp-pointed puncturing blades inclosed within a jointed covering sheath.

4-LINED
LEAF-BUG

Where plant bugs are common (and they are usually common) one may, by approaching cautiously, observe some of them standing quietly with the tip of the beak inserted into the substance of the leaf. This is not spectacular feeding, as compared with that of caterpillars and grasshoppers. It does not at once reduce the plant to

[41]

"rags and tatters." The little punctures scarcely show after the bug is gone; but the sap has been withdrawn, and the plant impoverished, and its growth thereby checked. Later the punctures may turn brown, and, if numerous, the leaf may die. If enough sap has been taken, the tissues will shrivel, and the whole plant may collapse. Chinch bugs feed in this manner; and every farmer knows too well the havoc of their sap-sucking in the corn field.

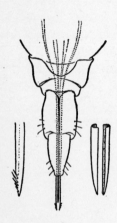

BEAK OF A BUG

This simple little beak, that every true bug (Hemipteran) carries concealed under its head, is nature's most widely used instrument for sap-gathering. It is of great economic importance.

Though the young of plant bugs are similar to adults in form and habits, in some of our injurious species they differ markedly in color. The common four-lined, plant bug of our gardens that as an adult is greenish with four black stripes laid lengthwise upon its back, is in its youth strongly marked with bright red and black; and two species of apple red-bugs, both dull colored as adults, have young of a tomato-red hue.

The females of plant bugs also possess an ovipositor, but it is a short one, and it is carried mostly concealed at the tip end of the body. It is used for cutting holes into the pith cavities of stems and placing eggs there. Any time after mid-summer, until they hatch the follow-

[42]

ing spring, the eggs of the four-lined leaf bug may be sought in the topmost twigs of currant bushes in the garden. They are inserted six to eight of them close together in a line; and because their white tips are a little exposed, they are not hard to find when common. Here again, the method of control is to gather and destroy the infested twigs.

The leaf hoppers are such dainty little insects, so light-footed, so swift of wing, so prettily colored, and so delicately built, it is hard to realize at first their capacity for injury. But when, as a result of their feeding, all the leaves of the grape vines shrivel and turn brown, or when the tops of all the potatoes in the garden rows are blasted with "tip burn," then we begin to realize what it means. In many a pasture the little unnoticed leaf hoppers get about as much forage from the grass as do the cattle.

VINE LEAF-HOPPER

SOME COMMON CATERPILLARS

The greatest consumers of green herbage on the earth are the caterpillars. These are the larvae of moths and butterflies. There are between five thousand and ten thousand different kinds of caterpillars in North America. Each kind has its favorite food plants. There is hardly a green thing growing on the land but has its own caterpillar enemies. Some plants have many of them, each  kind of caterpillar eating in its own place and time; some on leaf and some on root; some early and some late in the season; some on one kind of plant only and some feeding on several or many kinds of plants.

Most caterpillars feed on wild plants, and we take little notice of them; but many of them attack our growing crops. Some of these have been known as enemies from the beginning of recorded history. They all have biting mouthparts and chew their food. The general remedy, therefore, is food poisons (arsenicals).

However, some of them are borers, and live within the plants, where their food is not exposed, and where poisons cannot be applied to it; these have to be treated by other methods.

Caterpillars spin silk. That is one of their most characteristic activities. They spin a little when young, and a great deal when grown, in making their cocoons, preparatory to transformation. Silk worms are caterpillars that make huge cocoons of fine strong threads of white silk, loosely wound. We take advantage of their labors, and unwind the threads and weave them into our silk and satin textiles. One species only is cultivated for its silk, and it is an Oriental, not a native species. The big brown cocoons of our native American silk worms, we have not learned how to use profitably.

Caterpillars are mostly wormlike, and more or less similar in form to the cabbage worm shown on page fifteen. They have very small jointed legs on the three segments of the body immediately behind the head (thorax), and short fleshy prolegs (or prop legs) beneath some of the hinder segments (abdomen). Each of these prolegs bears a circlet of minute hooks (crotchets) at its tip. All these are used for creeping.

Generally, there is a brown horny plate of armor covering the first segment behind the head. There are bristles in definite arrangement on the skin of the body segments. Some caterpillars, like the black-and-brown banded "wooly bear" (larva of the Isabella moth) are densely hairy. There are endless variations in caterpillars.

Caterpillars are so numerous in kind and so varied in form that it is quite impossible to attempt to describe many of them here; so, we will content ourselves with mentioning three groups that have received common names. They represent three of the most important families of moths. We call them horn worms, span worms, and cut worms.

Horn worms are the larvae of the sphinx (or humming-bird) moths. They are large caterpillars when grown. The next to last segment of the body bears a decorative

TOMATO HORN-WORM

horn or tubercle, pointing backward. Among the best known among them are the tomato and tobacco horn worms. These, when disturbed, have a habit of lifting the front end of the body in a stiff, sphinx-like attitude. They go into the ground to transform; and unlike nearly all other moth caterpillars, they make no cocoon but remain naked pupae in their earthen cells. They are frequently turned up with the plow in garden soil. In these pupae the tongue-case remains free from the body (not soldered down tight, as in other chrysalids) giving them the peculiar, "jug-handle" appearance shown in our figure.

Other important horn worms are those of the modest sphinx, pale green in color, three inches long when grown, and commonly found feeding on poplar and cottonwood; Harris' sphinx, green and white striped like the pine needles among which it lies and on which it feeds, with only a small tubercle in place of the horn; the hog caterpillar that feeds on grape vines, two inches long when grown, with a white stripe along each side from head to horn, and seven short oblique stripes lower down on each side.

These horn worms are large enough and conspicuous enough to be controlled in a home garden by hand picking.

Span worms, or "measuring worms," or "loopers" are rather small caterpillars that have no legs under the middle of the body, but only at the ends. They do not creep like ordinary caterpillars, but proceed with a series of loopings, attaching the two ends alternately, arching the body high between them, and then straightening it out with a push forward. They thus travel by a method so peculiar that it is everywhere well-known. Superstitious folk will tell you when they see a looper laying off its lengths on your shoulder, that you the being measured for a new suit.

Among the important measuring worms are the canker-worms, of which we have two species, one for the spring and one for the fall, that do much damage to fruit trees and shade trees. The adult fe-male canker worms are wingless, and being hatched on or near the ground, they have to climb the trees to lay their eggs. There-fore, bands of some sticky sub-stance are commonly placed around tree trunks to keep the females

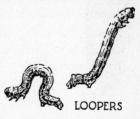

LOOPERS

from going up: tar, "tangle foot," or other substance, is used for this.

Another is the currant span-worm, a bright yellow caterpillar about an inch long when grown, with white lines on the sides and many minute black spots and dots. Another is the evergreen span-worm, that feeds on the leaves of pines, spruces and hemlocks. It is reddish above, with two pairs of white hairlines on its yellowish sides.

Cut worms and their kin are larvae of the owlet moths. They are mostly smooth caterpillars, longitudinally striped, of medium or large size. Those that are best known to the gardener have the wasteful habit of cutting off his peas and other plants at the surface of the ground, eating only the bit cut out of the stem, and leaving the top to die. They do this work at night, and hide by day beneath the surface of the soil.

A very important member of this family is the cotton worm of the South. Next to the boll weevil, this is the most important cotton pest. It eats the leaves. It reproduces very rapidly, there being five or six generations in a season.

Another well-known member of this family is the army worm. This is a native of meadows and pastures in the eastern United States. When it becomes very numerous, the caterpillars migrate in vast numbers (like an army, whence the name), and ravage grain fields. The grown larva is an inch long, and is striped with yellow, black and green.

Another pest that is a member of this family is the corn-ear worm. This is a borer in the tips of the ears of corn. It is especially destructive to sweet corn, and also bores in the bolls of cotton, and in the buds and flower stalks of tobacco.

These are a few of the more destructive members of three very large groups of moths. There are many other destructive caterpillars. Long ago, we had the misfortune to import into this country from Europe two that are proving very hard to control; the gypsy moth and the brown-tail moth caterpillars. Both eat the leaves of a great many plants, especially of trees and shrubs. Both first became established in New England. When they began to multiply and spread they seemed to threaten the

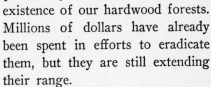

existence of our hardwood forests. Millions of dollars have already been spent in efforts to eradicate them, but they are still extending their range.

The gypsy moth larva is blackish in color, cross-lined with pale yellow. There are spiny, rounded tubercles on its back in pairs; the first five pairs of these are bluish and the others are reddish. The side tubercles of the body bear longer hairs. This larva devours the leaves of nearly all kinds of forest and fruit trees, and shrubs.

The brown-tail larvae have a similar wide range of diet except that they will not eat the leaves of conifers (pines, spruces, and other

EGG MASSES →

GIPSY MOTH
(½ X)

cone-bearing trees). The grown larva is an inch and a half long, blackish in color, clothed with brownish hairs, white-tufted at the sides. There are red tubercles on the middle of the back. Some of the barbed hairs that are

BROWN-TAIL
MOTH
($\frac{1}{2}$×)

CATERPILLAR

borne on these tubercles are poisonous, and when they penetrate the human skin they cause an inflammation that looks somewhat like ivy poisoning and that is known as "brown-tail rash." This unpleasant quality makes the brown-tail larvae very undesirable residents of a community. As a control measure the nests in which the larvae over-winter are collected and burned.

Still more recently the European corn borer has come to our shores. It was first found in Massachusetts in 1917. A careful survey in 1918 showed that it had over-spread an area of about four hundred square miles around Boston. A quarter of a million dollars was spent that year in an unsuccessful attempt to exterminate it, and many millions have been spent since in trying to stop its spread. It has moved westward, threatening great injury to our largest field crop, Indian corn.

It is a pale slender caterpillar, less than an inch long when grown. It lives inside the corn stalks, or sometimes in the ear, where it cannot be reached with food poisons. It is best controlled by burning or otherwise destroying the corn stubble and fallen stalks and weed stems in which it spends the winter.

[50]

SOME LEAF–EATING BEETLES

The most important leaf-eating insects are grasshoppers, caterpillars and beetles. We have been considering the first two of these; let us now consider the beetles.

Beetles are easily distinguished from other kinds of insects by their horny front wings that meet in a straight line down the middle of the back, forming a hard shell. There are more kinds of beetles than of any other sort of insect. They are adapted to live in every kind of place. They are grouped together in many "families." A few are so important as leaf eaters that we ought to be acquainted with them.

There is one "family" so generally given to the habit of eating green vegetation that it is known as the family of leaf beetles. The Colorado potato beetle is a member of this family that is known to every gar- dener. This is a shining oval beetle a quarter of an inch long, yellow in color, striped lengthwise down the back with black. Its larvae are short-legged, hump-backed creatures, orange or reddish in color, with black dots along the sides. Adults and larvae

COLORADO
POTATO-BEETLE

feed together openly upon the potato plants. Both are conspicuous, ill-smelling, "leaky" creatures. When disturbed a yellowish, offensive secretion is poured out from the glands of the skin. This is distasteful to birds and therefore highly protective. The beetles are safest when in plain sight, for then the birds let them severely alone.

In the spring the adult beetles come forth from their winter quarters in the ground, and lay their yellowish orange eggs in small clusters on the under side of the new potato leaves. These eggs hatch in about a week. The young larvae begin at once to feed upon the leaves. They eat away the margins, giving the leaves a ragged appearance. They grow and molt their skins four times, becoming more hump-backed and more conspicuous with each moult.

When grown they creep down the stem and enter the soil and transform there to pupae. Some two weeks later they reappear on the plants as adult beetles. Again eggs are laid, for a second brood is reared each season. The adults of the second brood are the ones we see in the fall or in early spring.

Potato beetles are controlled by arsenicals placed on the leaves. Hand picking is practical when there are only a few plants to be protected, because the pests, unlike most other injurious insects, are easily found.

COMMON ASPARAGUS
BEETLE

Very similar in general habits and life history is the asparagus beetle. It is more slender, and is marked showily with red, yellow and black. Its eggs are black. They are set up on end, singly, on the new asparagus shoots as these spring from the ground. Both adults and larvae at first eat holes in the shoots; later

[52]

they eat the skin off the full grown plants. This beetle is controlled by arsenicals and by clean cutting of the asparagus, leaving it no food.

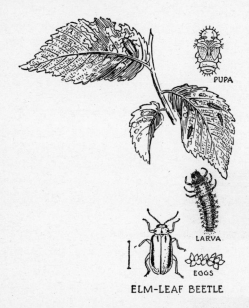

ELM-LEAF BEETLE

The imported elm-leaf beetle is, in the eastern United States, an important member of this group, destroying the foliage of many of our fine old elms. It is of a brownish yellow color, with obscure blackish stripes, one on each side of its back. Adults and larvae feed together upon the leaves.

It is controlled by arsenical sprays, thoroughly applied, when the trees are coming into full leaf.

The cucumber beetle has larvae that burrow beneath the ground in stem and roots. The adult is a black-headed

STRIPED
CUCUMBER-BEETLE

yellow beetle, broadly striped with black. It is about one-fifth of an inch long. It flies readily, and seeks out the seedling cucumbers when they first appear above the ground, and does its worst damage to them when they are little. The larva is a slender, whitish, worm-like creature with a double-pointed tip on the hind end of its body.

It is controlled by protective screen covers placed over the plants while they are small.

Among the leaf beetles there are some that have powerful muscular thighs on the hind legs that confer great powers of jumping. When disturbed, they will spring away suddenly a distance of several feet. They are therefore not inappropriately called flea-beetles. They may be recognized by their agility; nothing else jumps as they do. They are small beetles, some of them very small, mere specks as one sees them on the leaves, mostly of dark color, often black. They are real pests in the garden, for they eat numerous pits and holes in the leaves of many kinds of plants, and the leaves then turn brown and die.

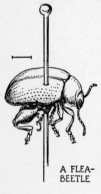

A FLEA-
BEETLE

When the larvae and adults feed openly together (as in the case of the grape-vine flea-beetle), the larvae have blackish head and legs, and a paler skin beset with black dots and dashes, bearing spiny tubercles. When only the adults feed on the leaves, and the larvae feed within the stems or on the roots under

[54]

ground, then the larvae are pale and more or less naked. The potato flea-beetle is one of the latter sort; its larvae, an eighth or an inch long when grown, make minute surface pits in the roots and tubers of potatoes. The adult black beetle is one of the smallest of the flea-beetles.

The potato flea-beetle attacks cucumbers, egg-plants, peppers, turnips, radishes, cabbages, celery, beets and petunias, having a wide range of diet. Most flea-beetles confine themselves to very few kinds of plants.

Another great group of leaf-eating beetles is represented by the May beetles ("June bugs"), goldsmith beetles, sugar-cane beetles, leaf chafers, and others, whose larvae are known as "white grubs" and live on the roots in the soil. They are large, clumsy beetles with spiny legs, and a noisy, humming flight. They are variously colored and shaped, but they all have one curious character in common; the knob of the antenna is composed of a number of thin, flat plates, close-laid, side by side.

MAY-BEETLE

A very undesirable alien belonging to this group is the Japanese beetle that made its appearance in New Jersey in 1916. It feeds on the foliage of most plants, having a very wide range of diet; and its grub feeds on roots. Great efforts have been made to prevent its spread, but it seems to be slowly creeping westward.

Now we will speak of three great groups of beetles that are so handsome in form and coloring and sculpturing that they are the delight of collectors of beautiful specimens. These are the groups to show to non-entomological friends. When properly arranged and labelled in the collector's cabinet they bear the imposing Greek names, Cerambycidae, Buprestidae and Elateridae; but we will here call them Long Horn, and Short Horn, and Click Beetles. The adults of all three groups eat leaves, but their larvae feed mainly upon the trunks and bark and roots of plants, big and little.

LOCUST BORER

The Long Horn Beetles are mostly showily patterned in great variety. The first segment of the thorax is rounded at the sides, and the antennae are long, sometimes much longer than the body: not so, however, in the locust borer, shown herewith. This beetle is often to be found in late summer and autumn clambering over the flower clusters of golden rod, eating pollen, and may easily be picked by hand. Its larva is a so-called round head borer (see figure on p. fifty-eight) that bores in the wood of the trunks of locust trees doing great damage to them.

FLAT-HEADED
APPLE-TREE BORER

The Short Horn Borers are exceedingly hard-shelled beetles of stockier build, and often of brilliant metallic coloration. The one shown herewith is an important pest of the apple orchard. Its larva is more or less tadpole shaped in outline, with the wide head end much flattened. This widening accommodates some very strong

[56]

and unusually large jaw muscles. It is able to eat its way through very hard wood.

The Click Beetles are mostly rather small and slender, with a somewhat flattened body that tapers toward both ends, and that has a peculiar loose and very flexible middle joint by which the group is most easily known. The owl beetle herewith shown is an exceptionally large member of the group; exceptional also for the startling color pattern on its back.

The click beetles are also called "skip-jacks." They are the acrobats of the beetle world. Touch a live one and it instantly folds its legs and antennae close against its body and falls down as if dead. If it lands on its back it lies there for a time, and then, its legs still tightly folded, with a clicking sound it springs several inches into the air and falls again. If it alights on its feet it then runs away: if not, it springs up again and again until successful in getting right side up again.

This is a very curious and interesting performance, that is provided for at the flexible middle joint of the body. Placed on its back the beetle lifts its body up on its two ends. Then suddenly snapping downward in the middle against its solid support it rebounds into the air.

The larvae of the click beetles are known as wire worms. They are hard-shelled, smoothly-cylindrical, brown in color from end to end, and generally bear a flattened

OWL BEETLE

and variously toothed plate on the tail end. They live mostly in rotten wood or in the soil. The owl beetle is one of the largest of them. Its larva is often found in rotten tree trunks.

STRIPED BLISTER-BEETLE

The blister beetles represent another group whose members feed as adults on potatoes and other garden vegetables. They are long-legged beetles with narrow bodies, half an inch long or more, and with loose-fitting wings. The various kinds are differently colored, but they all have one characteristic shape. They fly readily, and move forward together in companies, often completely destroying vegetation as they go. They are not eaten by birds, for when disturbed they secrete an acrid, yellowish fluid that is very disagreeable. In contact with the human skin it produces blisters.

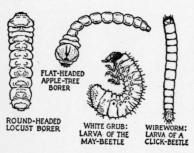

ROUND-HEADED LOCUST BORER
FLAT-HEADED APPLE-TREE BORER
WHITE GRUB: LARVA OF THE MAY-BEETLE
WIREWORM: LARVA OF A CLICK-BEETLE

It is only the adults that are injurious. The larvae of most blister beetles are unknown; but those of the striped blister beetle shown in our figure eat grasshopper eggs. Here, then, we have the unusual thing: An insect beneficial as a larva and injurious as an adult insect.

The snout beetles and weevils are another group of herbivorous beetles of very great importance and of very remarkable form. The front of the head is prolonged into a beak that carries the jaws out at its tip, and the

[58]

elbowed antennae, part way down its sides. The jaws chew, as in other beetles; but swallowing is more of a task in these, and a pair of food rammers, projecting down from the base of the jaws, is developed inside the gullet to start the food along.

These are mostly small, hard-shelled beetles. Many of them feign death when disturbed, and drop to the ground, and lie with legs closely folded, hidden among the trash.

This is an enormous group. Its members are alert to find every sort of vegetable food: roots, stems and leaves; buds, flowers and fruits; nuts, seeds and grain; galls, bark and solid wood. Fortunately for us, most species are restricted in their diet. They eat of a single kind of plant, or of a few closely related plants. The adult female seeks out the plant that will furnish food suitable for her young, gnaws a hole convenient to the substances that will serve as infant food, and then leaves her egg in the hole.

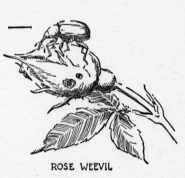

ROSE WEEVIL

The larvae of snout beetles are short and fat with well-arched bodies. They have very short legs or no legs at all. A few of them, like the clover leaf weevil and the alfalfa weevil live and feed openly upon the leaves. The name "weevil" is more especially applied to those that feed on seeds and grains. "Curculio" is the name applied to those that infest fruits.

One of the most familiar forms is the common rose

weevil. It is a handsome snout beetle, a quarter of an inch long, red above (except the long snout) and black

GRANARY WEEVIL

below. It is commonly seen upon single roses, eating holes in their petals, and spoiling them. It eats also into the developing fruit beneath the flower, and there it lays its eggs. Its larvae feed upon the seeds in the rose-hip, avoiding the soft, sweet pulp. We can find them easily by splitting the rose-hips open in autumn.

Another that is common about our gardens is the stiff, awkward appearing, rusty brown rhubarb weevil.

COTTON BOLL WEEVIL

The worst of flower destroying forms is the strawberry weevil which lays its eggs in the flower bud, and then cuts off the flower stalk, leaving its larva to develop in the fallen bud. The worst stored-grain-eaters are the granary weevil, which infests wheat, and the rice weevil.

Among the snout beetles are many of our most serious pests. The cotton boll weevil is an example. This species came to us about 1890 from Mexico, by way of Texas; and it has spread all over the cotton belt, doing incalculable damage to this most important crop. Both adults and larvae attack the cotton bolls, the latter from within, eating the seeds.

Control of these insects is not an easy matter. Arsenical food poisons are more or less effective with those that feed openly, and are much used. They need to be supplemented in most cases by cultural methods based on accurate knowledge of the habits of the weevil in all stages. One of the most generally useful of cultural control methods is the destruction of the trash in which the weevils live through the winter.

SCALE INSECTS AND APHIDS

Here are two groups of sucking insects that will make no appeal to the collector who is seeking merely beautiful specimens, but they are worthy of study because of their very great economic importance. No net is required to catch them. They cannot run. They are generally collected by bringing in the bough on which they are found; and they are often found so thickly infesting a plant as to almost cover it. Specimens of both groups maybe preserved in alcohol.

Both are small; but they make up in reproductive capacity what they may lack in size. A single scale or aphid can drain but little sap from a tree, but the hordes of them that gather upon it, all with their sap pumps working, may drain it to death.

Both are fixed in place and both are gregarious. Lacking good powers of locomotion, they increase and remain together in numbers. Wild and cultivated plants alike are infested by them. Both occur in greenhouses, and some of them may be found there for study in the winter season.

Fortunately for us, both scales and aphids are very limited in the range of their diet; each kind will live on only a few kinds of plants. Many of them are named from the plants they infest; as cabbage aphis, cherry aphis, rose-apple aphis, peach scale, and elm scale. Some members of both groups secrete from pores along the sides of the body a whitish wax that gives them a peculiar fluffy appearance, from which are derived other common names, such as cottony cushion-scale, and woolly aphis of the apple. Two of our worst scale-insect pests were named for other reasons: The San Jose scale, because the first of its depredations to be made known were near that city in California; the oyster shell scale, because of its shape and color.

Scale insects are often called "bark lice." Our figure shows the appearance of one of them on the twigs of plum in spring. They are flattened in form, nearly or quite motionless, and quite inanimate looking, with all legs and other appendages concealed beneath the flaring edges of a wrinkled, scale-like back. The back is variously fluted and sculptured. The male scales are very much smaller than the female.

Eggs in great numbers are produced within the bodies of the large female scales—indeed, the soft body within seems to be wholly used up in egg pro-
duction; and from underneath the old shell at the proper season multitudes of very minute young scales issue. These are more active; and on their

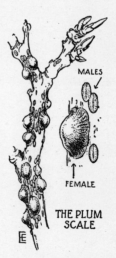

MALES

FEMALE

THE PLUM
SCALE

relatively longer legs they creep out onto the fresh green shoots, where they settle and insert their little beaks and begin to feed.

These thin-skinned young scales may be killed by ordinary contact poisons, to which the heavily armored old scales are quite resistant. The old scales are commonly treated with a strong lime-sulfur wash, or with oil emulsions (such as "Scalecide"). These being injurious to green leaves, may be applied only before the buds have begun to swell in the spring. The twig shown in our figure has already advanced too far to permit safe lime-sulfur application.

Aphids are also called "plant lice," but the name is inappropriate for they are not lice.

Aphids are mostly greenish in color, but those commonly seen on pasture thistles in autumn are blackish, and those on goldenrods and golden-glow are red. They are a little more active than scale insects. They will stiffly walk about on their food plant if disturbed. We see them sitting in companies on a green leaf, feeding, all headed in the same direction, be it up or down; big and little, old and young intermingled, and most of them with their beaks inserted to the hilt all the time. They are miniature sap pumps.

If we examine them under a lens we find here and there one with its beak inserted so deeply that its body is tilted forward, and its hind legs lifted blissfully into the air. If we then disturb such an one we can see the hind feet let down and the beak withdrawn and slung backward beneath the head. And when it seeks to get away from our disturbance and clambers over its fellows, we can see them kicking at it as a trespasser.

During the greater part of the season the aphid colony is composed of females only. They give birth to living young, a new one being born every few hours. These young ones develop so rapidly that in a very short time they in turn begin to produce young ones, and thus the colony grows with astonishing rapidity.

The cabbage aphis averages a generation every 12 2/5 days, with the females each producing about forty-one

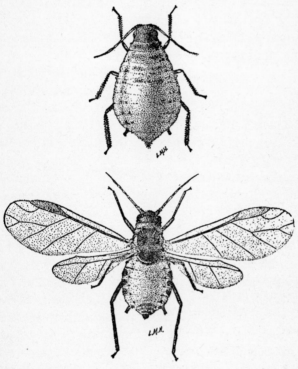

young, according to studies made by Professor G. W. Herrick. He calculates that if all the young produced from a single female were to survive for twelve generations, that generation would number 564,087,257,509,-

154,652 individuals, whose weight would be more than 822,000,000 tons. Of course, comparatively few survive; excessive offspring provide against excessive losses. But the possibilities of such increase are there, and at times, when all conditions are favorable, a plague of aphids comes on with great suddenness.

Aphids are helpless creatures. They have many enemies, and but feeble means of escape from any of them. Conspicuous among their enemies are three other groups of insects; lady-bird beetles, aphis lions, and syrphus-fly larvae.

LADYBIRD-BEETLE   LARVA

Lady-bird beetles in both larval and adult stages feed on both scales and aphids. The adults are very familiar little insects, more or less hemispherical in form with the legs attached beneath the flat side, in bright coats that shine as if newly varnished, bearing conspicuous black or red or yellow spots. There are many kinds of them, and many variants of color and pattern. Their larvae are less easily recognizable, but they are all more or less like the one shown in our figure.

It was a lady-bird beetle that was imported into California in 1888, and that checked the ravages of the cottony cushion-scale, and saved the citrus industry of that state from destruction. Against such enemies the aphids and scales can offer hardly any resistance.

The "aphis lion" is the larva of the lace-wing fly—a slender, delicate green insect with transparent, gauzy wings, and shining golden eyes. The fly is often seen about the lights on our porches at night. The larva is a sprawling, spiny-backed creature, with immense jaws as long as the head. These jaws project forward, pincher-like. They are perforated from tip to base and lead to the gullet inside the head. The larva sucks the blood of an aphid through these two tubes as we might suck a soda through two straws. Driving the tip of both tubes into the body of

APHIS-LION

a stupid but juicy aphid, the aphis lion lifts it aloft on their points, and holds it there helpless while drinking its blood; and when this is done, it throws the empty skin aside and goes after another one.

The adult lace-wing has ordinary toothed jaws, and such aphids as it eats, it chews and swallows, as do the lady-birds.

The larvae of some of the syrphus flies may also often be found in the aphid colony, foraging. They are soft, legless larvae of an inconspicuous greenish or grayish coloration,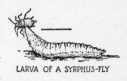

LARVA OF A SYRPHUS-FLY

that are able to creep by adhesion over the leaves. They strike their two sharp mouth-hooks together into the side of an aphid, and tear it loose from its moorings, and hold it aloft while sucking its blood.

Aphids have other more minute but no less dangerous enemies. Besides the big predators just mentioned that feed upon them openly, there are parasites that feed within the body consuming its substance. In almost any populous aphid colony it is easy to find empty skins with gaping holes in the back;

APHID SKIN FROM WHICH A PARASITE HAS EMERGED.

holes from which the parasites that killed the aphid emerged.

On the other hand, aphids have a few friends in the insect world. Here in our figure is shown a colony of aphids under the protection of friendly ants. In summer or autumn on many a curled dock or thistle, or wherever ants are seen gathered together upon green foliage, there you may expect to find with closer looking an abundance of aphids as well. And if you approach quietly and watch carefully you may see the ants moving about

among the aphid herd, fondling them with their antennae, patting or stroking an individual here and there, and obtaining sometimes as a response a drop of honey dew. The aphid discharges the drop, and the ant laps it up eagerly. In return for this the ants protect the aphid colony. You may often see them drive away such intruders as winged parasitic insects that seek to lay their eggs upon the bodies of the aphids. If you attempt to touch the aphids the ants will even rush at your finger and attempt to bite it.

MOSQUITOS

When you wish to collect a few specimens of mosquitos you need only to sit out
of doors in a sheltered place on a summer
evening; for they are very fond of you,
and will soon come to you and linger
caressingly near.

If it be early twilight, with light enough
remaining, you may learn something by watching one of
them through a complete performance. Placing your bare
hand on some stationary support that is convenient for
observation, you may see a mosquito settle on it, and give
a demonstration in expert surgery. How gently it lets
itself down on its six, long, slender, soft-padded feet!
How quickly it unslings its long beak, and applies the tip
of it to your skin! How easily the slender stylets in the
beak begin to penetrate!

Now is the time to preserve your self-control, to restrain
all violent impulses to swat or to swear, and to maintain
a calm, dignified, philosophical, observant attitude.

Deeper go the stylets into the skin; their sheath is turned
aside; the head descends, gauging the depth of probing.
A little inconsequential stinging sensation marks the injec-
tion of saliva into the wound; this will promote the free-
flowing of your blood. Then the sucking begins; a rhyth-

mic pulsation of the mosquito's body accompanies the up-flowing of blood. How gently it flows! What a pretty performance! Only a drop or two is needed to equip this sanguinary little beast for life, and you can well spare it in exchange for such an admirable exhibition of skill. Soon

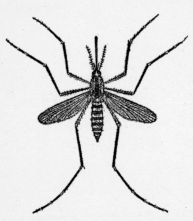

the tiny red stream expands the capacious stomach and a faint tinge of red begins to show through the transparent sutures of the bag-like abdomen. Then the beak is suddenly withdrawn; and with a tiny, high-pitched whir of wings the beastie is gone!

Being fully satisfied with this one performance, you should next use your cyanide bottle to take a few specimens indoors for closer examination. What delicate creatures they are; how slender and fragile! Their flight is so weak they cannot withstand a breeze; hence they trouble you very little in open places. Their wings are fringed with scales along the veins and this (as well as their biting) will distinguish them from midges and other similar two-winged flies. Unless you use the slenderest of pins, you cannot well pin them through the body in the ordinary way without splitting them; but you may mount them on a pinpoint that is thrust through a piece of white cardboard, as indicated in our figure.

All the specimens in our bottle will be females, for only the females bite. If you want males you will have to go after them, for they do not come after you. You can get both sexes by sweeping with a collecting net the vegetation where they rest by day, or by taking them overhead in an open cyanide bottle from beneath bridge timbers, or shed roofs, or other similar shelters. The males are even more slender than the females, and are easily distinguished by the brush of long, soft hairs that clothes the base of the antennae.

MOSQUITO
ADULT FEMALE

There are two common kinds of mosquitos that you should be able to recognize on sight: malarial and non-malarial. Both are annoying because they both bite; but the former are dangerous. They often carry the germs of malaria; and when an infected malarial mosquito bites you it injects into the blood, along with its own saliva, the germs that may develop in your red blood corpuscles, causing the chills and fevers that characterize that disease. Malarial mosquitos have spotted wings; non-malarial have unspotted wings. It is only the latter that you should allow to bite you, even for an object lesson. The others (which, fortunately, are more strictly nocturnal) should be well screened against.

Mosquitos develop in the water. In stagnant, weedy pools and ditches that are not permanent, in rain-water

[71]

barrels and open cisterns and all such places, they abound. Fishes are their natural enemies; so they thrive best where there are no fishes.

Their young are commonly known as "wrigglers." You can find them by searching such stagnant waters with

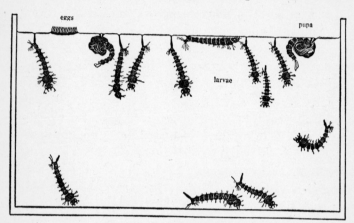

a dip-net (see page 107). Or, you can make a mosquito hatchery of your own to order very simply: If you put a teaspoonful of milk in half a gallon of water and expose it overnight in an open dish where adult mosquitos abound, the females will probably come and lay their eggs on the surface of the water in the dish. The eggs will be found floating in little rafts upon the surface. Those of the malarial mosquito float flatwise; those of the commoner non-malarial ones are placed vertically in a single compact layer. They will probably hatch in a few days, and will appear in the water as minute "wrigglers" swimming about jerkily, tail first. They will feed upon the milk particles that are distributed through the water, and will grow up to the form shown in our figure.

If you put some well-grown "wrigglers" into a glass tumbler, you may, by watching their behavior, get a clue to the methods of control. When they are undisturbed, you will see that they remain quietly at the surface, taking air. The slender, smooth tube at the rear end of the body, that breaks through the surface film of the water, is a breathing tube. You can see indistinctly that the two long air trunks that run through the body terminate in it. They can take air only at the surface. Kerosene oil, even in very small quantities, when spread upon the surface of the water, clogs their breathing apparatus and suffocates them.

The larvae, or "wrigglers" of the common non-malarial mosquitos (*Culex*) hang well beneath the surface, with the head end extended obliquely downward when at rest. Those of the malarial mosquitos (*Anopheles*) lie horizontally, close to the surface, and at the rear end of their body there is very little development of the breathing tube. These, also, are more given to feeding on floating food materials. Their necks are exceedingly rubbery, allowing the head to be rotated very freely. In feeding it is held at a half rotation, mouth up, while the jaw-brushes sweep in floating food particles. Hence, aeroplanes are used in the South for spreading poisonous dusts upon the surface of swamps and ponds for the larvae of these malarial mosquitos to eat.

When the larvae are grown they transform into pupae that are also "wrigglers." These are remarkably active pupae, very unlike the inert chrysalids of butterflies. They also hang at the surface when quiet, and swim down below out of danger when disturbed. The breathing tube at the rear end of the body has been lost, and a pair of ear-like respiratory horns at the front of the body has been developed instead. So, the pupae in taking air at the surface hangs front end upward, with these horns penetrating the surface film. Hence the pupae are likewise subject to suffocation by oil on the surface.

Spraying the surface of the pools with kerosene is an effective measure against mosquitos; but it is only temporarily effective. The film of oil must be renewed about every two weeks during the mosquito season. Permanent control is obtained by draining temporary pools, and by covering cisterns, rain-water barrels, plumbing traps, and all such water containers, with wire-cloth screens. Bites of malarial mosquitos may be avoided by remaining inside screened quarters after dark. This is not necessary except in regions in which malaria is known to be prevalent.

SOME INSECTS THAT EAT OUR FOODS

There are some insects that like to share our food with us, and that can adapt themselves to our way of living.

Noteworthy among these are the cockroaches, that nobody loves; flat, smooth, shiny, wingless, brownish, crevice-haunting insects, that run rapidly, and smell badly, and always shun the light. They are not too particular what they eat, taking kindly to many of the foods that our pantry affords. And their table manners are bad; they leave things in the sort of a mess that the neat housekeeper does not like.

Cockroaches lay their eggs in large, brown, oblong packages, all encased together in a horny shell. They leave these egg packets in the floor-crevices that are their runways. The young on hatching run and feed along with the old ones. They grow rapidly, and if given plenty of food and shelter, there will soon be hordes of them in the house.

There are inexpensive commercial traps for cockroaches that are fairly successful when baited with attractive foods and placed convenient to the runways. Cockroaches may be suffocated by blowing very finely powdered borax into their runways with a powder-gun.

The house fly is about the only insect that is much observed by day in our dwellings. The fly takes liquid foods through its peculiar beak. It takes solid foods, like sugar, by first dissolving them in a drop of its own saliva, and then sucking up the solution. We may see this easily, if, instead of swatting them with our first impulse, we sit down and watch them feed—say, on a lump of sugar, placed conveniently for the purpose. We will first see the two flaps at the tip of the beak applied to the sugar; then we will see the sucking movements; and then, when it is done, we will see the little pit on the surface, whence the sugar has been removed.

Until recently, flies have been tolerated rather generally as comparatively harmless pests; but now we know that they often carry the germs of typhoid fever and of other diseases, and distribute these germs with their feet. So we have come to regard them as dangerous enemies, that are to be excluded from our houses.

The only truly effective way to reduce fly population is to cut it off at its source. The fly lays its eggs out of doors in decaying organic substances. A favorite place is a manure pile beneath some stable window. In horse manure the soft, white, headless larvae (maggots) thrive amazingly, and in warm weather, yield a fine new crop of flies in less than two weeks from the laying of the eggs. Therefore, remove the breeding places, or screen them in. Shut out the flies from houses by screens; kill such as get indoors, with strips of "tangle-foot," or with a poisoned drink (such as a tablespoon of formaldehyde in half a pint of water), exposed conveniently for them in a saucer.

Ants maintain their households mainly outside our houses, and come inside only to find food. There are several very different kinds of ants that get into our pantries: big, black carpenter ants, and ordinary red ants, and very little, faded-looking atoms of ants—the kind that mix

[76]

so smoothly with our apple-sauce! Everybody knows ants; so, there is no need to describe them. The world is full of them.

By way of control, remove indoor attractions for them by keeping foods in tight containers. Locate their nests, and open them up, and pour into them a spoonful of carbon bisulphide (see p. one hundred and four). Bait them (as with tartar emetic 1 part, sugar 10 parts, water to moisten well), and so lure them to their death.

There are a number of competitors for our food supplies that live in the stored foods as larvae. The commonest of these are flour moths, flour beetles, meal worms, bean weevils, rice weevils, and cheese skippers. These will now be briefly described. For all of them the method of control is to keep foods in tight containers, and so shut them out. If they get in, fumigate the foods in a gastight box with carbon bisulphide.

Flour moths. The larvae are flesh-tinted caterpillars about half an inch long when grown, with the usual caterpillar legs and prolegs and bristly skin. They burrow through flour and other cereals, spinning threads as they go, and webbing the material together. The adults are grayish moths, the fore wings marked with brown, the hind wings paler, the end of the body upturned between the wing tips when these are closed.

Meal worms. The short-legged larvae are hard-shelled and cylindrical in form, brownish or yellowish in color and about an inch long when grown. They are found usually in the bottom or in the wall crevices of meal or grain bins. The adults are plain brownish beetles, half an inch long, having sixteen minute furrows running lengthwise of each wing cover.

[77]

Flour beetles. The cylindric, yellowish larvae look like miniature meal worms. They feed on flour and meal and package cereals, sometimes matting the material together, but not with spun threads. The adult beetles are only about an eighth of an inch in length, reddish brown in color, and pitted all over the back with numberless fine punctures.

PEA WEEVIL

Bean weevils. The curved, whitish larvae are found in stored beans. The adults are short-beaked snout-beetles a sixth of an inch long, having a body that tapers from the rear forward (when viewed from above), and wing covers mottled with obscure lighter and darker spots.

Rice weevils. The larvae are short, fat legless creatures that feed within grains of stored rice. The adults are plain grayish snout beetles about an eighth of an inch long.

Larder beetles. The larvae are spindle-shaped, hairy, short-legged creatures found on hams, bacon and other meats and on skins. The adults are oblong beetles with the ends symmetrically rounded and about a fourth of an inch long. They are dark brown, with a paler yellowish band across the basal half of the wing covers, and their short antennae are conspicuously knobbed at the tip.

Cheese skippers. These are legless, headless, soft, white maggots, the larvae of a shiny black fly that is half the size of a house fly. The larvae are remarkable for their ability to jump several inches by means of sudden bendings of the body. They live in cheese.

INSECTS THAT EAT OUR WOOLENS

There are some insects that eat hair—just plain, dry hair or fur, at every meal through all their lives. Such is the monotonous diet of the clothes moths. And it matters little to them whether the hair is spun, or loose, or woven: they eat it just the same. But it matters much to us if the hair be made up into new and costly garments and robes; so, it is worth while to know something about the possessors of this strange appetite.

There are three kinds of clothes moths that get into our wardrobes and eat our woolens and furs. The damage is all done by their larvae (small, pale, innocent-looking caterpillars) ; for the adults eat nothing, and live only long enough to lay their eggs. They are small moths, having a wing expanse of about three-quarters of an inch. The wings bear long fringes of scales about the hind margins, and the hind wings are pale. The larvae all spin silk, but in such different ways that they are all recognizable by their spinning work, as follows:

The case-bearing clothes-moth larva constructs a port-able case and lives inside it. The case is made of bits of wool stuck together with silk. It is a nearly cylindric tube, open at both ends. In feed-ing or traveling the larva ex-

CASE-BEARING CLOTHES-MOTH
LARVA

tends its head and legs at one end of the case. This larva as it grows has need to widen its case occasionally, and it does this in a very interesting way. It cuts a lengthwise slit and inserts a gore of new material. In the summer season, when the larva is growing rapidly, it can be induced to make for itself a coat of many colors, by supplying it on successive days with cloth of different colors, black, white, red or other colors; for it makes its repairs out of whatever wool is available, without regard to color scheme.

The fore wings of the adult moth are brown with a few darker spots on them.

The tapestry clothes moth larva makes a fixed tube, and not a portable case. The tube is made of silk mixed with fragments of its food. The larva lives, and later transforms, within this tube, which is spun by preference in coarser stuffs, such as tapestries, carpets, and furs.

The fore wings of the adult moth are black basally, and white on the outer half.

The naked clothes moth larva spins tangled threads of silk through the wool on which it feeds, without making either case or tube. When grown it spins a cocoon about itself, in which to transform, and this cocoon is covered with mixed silk and wool. This is the one that is most destructive to garments, especially in the South. The fore wings of the adult moth are of a delicate straw color, unspotted.

None of these above-mentioned larvae seems to have any of our difficulties distinguishing between cotton and wool when these are in a mixture in our textiles. They eat all the wool, and leave the cotton openly showing.

Carpet beetles also eat our woolens, but mostly the coarser sort, found in floor coverings. Here again it is the larvae that do all the damage; the adults feed upon the pollen of flowers. Two species are more or less common:

The imported carpet beetle (called also, sometimes, by the absurd name "buffalo moth"). The larva is an active spindle-shaped, short-legged creature a quarter of an inch long, bristling all over with stiff brown hairs. The adult is a minute black beetle, whose very convex back has a mottled appearance due to the presence of a scanty covering of black, white, and brick-red scales.

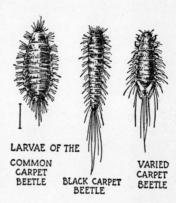

LARVAE OF THE

COMMON CARPET BEETLE   BLACK CARPET BEETLE   VARIED CARPET BEETLE

The black carpet beetle larva is more slender, and tapers to the rear, where it bears a tuft of extra long hairs trailing behind. The adult beetle is plain black.

Carpet beetles are most commonly found working on tacked-down carpets from the underside, along cracks in the floor, that afford shelter from the pressure of heavy feet above; also in stored rugs; also in furs, and dried skins; also, alas in dried insects. And among their kin are some of the worst museum pests. We have to guard our pinned insects from them by using tight boxes. For, if the adult beetles get in and lay their eggs on our specimens, soon we will see a brown dust falling on the bottom

[81]

underneath them, then legs and heads fall away, and then —bare pins!

Clothes moths and carpet beetles find their best chance of a livelihood in attics, closets, store-rooms, wood-sheds, and all such places where discarded scraps of woolens and furs are left undisturbed for a long time. To get material for study it is only necessary to search such places, and examine the stuff found in them. A cast off woolen coat or an old horse blanket may be breeding enough of these pests to stock a neighborhood.

Wherever woolen felt is used, as on the deadeners of piano keys, or on billiard table coverings, these pests may be destructive. We may get an idea of the extent of their damage in this nation by figuring the losses of garments and furnishings in our own home in dollars, and then multiplying that figure by the 20,000,000 homes in the entire country. It is a good big bill.

Control of all these demands that we leave no rubbish pile containing scraps of wool or fur for them to breed in. Put unused woolens and furs away for the summer season in tight, moth-proof containers. Cedar chests are not necessarily moth proof. Treated paper bags are often used. Expose used garments to the sunshine occasionally, and give them an occasional brushing. Fumigate infested goods with carbon bisulphide (see p. one hundred and four) in a gas-tight box. Pests that get into insect boxes may be killed by saturating a bit of sponge with carbon bisulphide, placing it inside and closing the box tightly for a day.

SOME INSECTS THAT EAT FRUIT AND NUTS

Fruits and nuts are among the choicest food products that Mother Nature has given her children. Certain insects have found this out and have come in for their share. Sometimes it is a very large share that they take. The loss demands that we take notice of the ways of these competitors, and so learn how to deal with them.

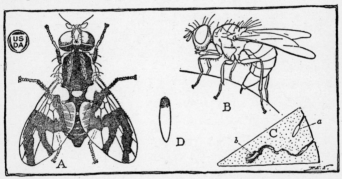

This book begins with a very brief account of the world's most widespread destroyer of fruit, the codling moth of the apple. Another cause of "wormy" apples is the apple maggot. This is the young of a very pretty little fly. It begins its activities much later in the season than the codling moth. The adult female appears in the apple trees in June. She seeks well-grown fruit in which to lay her eggs. With an egg-laying tool (an ovipositor) developed at the end of her body she makes a hole through the apple skin and into the pulp, and she lays an egg in the hole. The young maggot that hatches from this egg begins burrowing through the flesh at once, and is never exposed on the surface of the apple. So, it is safe from poison sprays and dust. The hole heals over, leaving

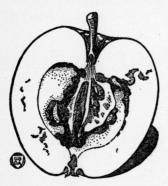 hardly a trace on the surface of the apple to tell what is going on inside. The maggot bores its way irregularly through the pulp. Its tunnels turn brown and are later followed by decay. And the apple, of course, is spoiled.

Since the maggot cannot be reached with poison, this pest is controlled by poisoning the fly before its eggs are laid. It feeds like a housefly by lapping up with the tip of its beak whatever food or water it finds on the surfaces of leaves and fruit. So, the poison (lead arsenate again, in either spray or dust) is spread thinly over the foliage. The flies eat it and die.

The time of putting on the poison is, again, very important. It must be done before the eggs are laid; and since the flies keep hatching out for a time, two sprayings are necessary for complete control. In the northern United States the times are: 1st, the closing days of June; and 2nd, the middle of July.

There are two very similar fruit flies whose larvae spoil cherries.

Here in America we recently had a bad scare over the arrival on our shores of a little foreign fruit fly that we considered to be a very undesirable immigrant, the Mediterranean fruit fly. It is probably the world's worst destroyer of citrus fruits (oranges, lemons, grapefruits, etc.). It was found in central Florida in April, 1929. How it got there no one knew. It had long been known as a destructive pest of fruits in other parts of the earth. In a number of countries the fruit-growing industries had been ruined by its ravages. It flourishes elsewhere in almost all subtropical fruit growing regions of the earth, and would doubtless spread to all our Southern and Southwestern states if let alone; for it is hardy and prolific and a good flier.

Soon after its discovery Congress appropriated $4,250,-000 toward the work of its extermination, and a real fight began, with all the forces of the United States Department of Agriculture and of all the southern fruit-growing states enlisted against it.

Yet it is only a fly—a pretty little fly about the size of a common housefly, with banded and spotted wings. The female fly drills holes through the skins of fruits, and deposits several eggs in each hole. These eggs soon hatch into little white worm-like larvae of the form called maggots. They are naked, and headless, and legless, and white and nearly transparent—very similar in form to the apple maggot, shown in the last figure. They are about a fourth of an inch long when full grown. These maggots burrow through the flesh of the fruit, causing it to decay.

It is an especial enemy to citrus fruits. It also attacks peaches, apricots, plums, grapes, apples, pears and many other fruits, both wild and cultivated. Since its larvae live only in fleshy fruits and in the warmer parts of the earth, the battle was waged against it by destroying all fruits both wild and tame in the entire area in Florida into which it had entered. The extermination of the pest from Florida is one of the triumphs of economic entomology. By it the citrus industry of the whole country has been saved for the present from its ravages.

Certain snout beetles also infest fruits. Probably the worst one in eastern North America is known as the plum curculio. It destroys mainly stone fruits (plums, cherries, peaches, etc.) but it also is counted among the pests of the apple. The adult is a warty-backed little weevil, brown in color, marked with gray and black. It eats a hole in the side of the green fruit and lays an egg in the hole. Then it cuts a little crescent-shaped groove in the skin of the fruit half way around the hole. This leaves a scar on the surface of the fruit by which the work of the curculio may later be distinguished from that of other insects. Out of the egg there develops a footless white larva with a brown head. It generally causes the fruit to drop before maturity.

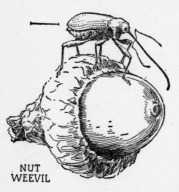

NUT
WEEVIL

Nuts are the neatest packages in which Mother Nature puts up her choice food stores for long keeping. They are thick-walled and tightly sealed packages, but some of the snout beetles have found a way to get into them. The longest

beaked of the snout beetles are the nut weevils that infest
nuts and acorns. The extremely long beak of the female
is used to bore a deep hole through the thick coverings of
the nuts, so that the larva, hatching from the egg which

is placed in the hole, may find easy access to its proper food.
At *a* in the accompanying figure is shown the adult chest-
nut weevil; at *b* a side view of the female and at *c* the
head of the male; at *d,* two eggs; at *e* a larva, such as is
too often found inside when cracking the nuts; at *f* and *g,*
two views of the pupa.

When the nuts fall to the ground the larva inside eats
a hole just large enough to get its head through, then
squeezes its fat body through, and goes down into the
ground for its transformation.

The making over of that little doll-faced head of the
larva into the beaked head of the adult beetle is an amazing
process, the externals of which may easily be seen as follows: When acorns first begin to drop gather up a quart
of them from the ground and put them in a glass jar. If
infested you will find in a very few days the white fat

larvae wriggling around in the corners at the bottom of the jar, and holes in some of the acorn shells. Throw the larvae in a pail or large jar of earth and set it indoors in

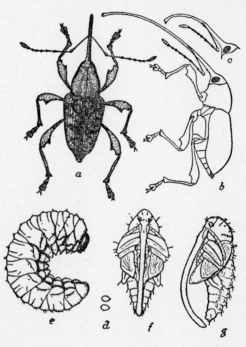

not too dry a place until next March. Then sift the earth and you will find that the larvae have become pupae with elephantine noses.

SOME CARNIVOROUS (FLESH–EATING) INSECTS

It is not the way of the world that these insect consumers of leaves and fruits and other products should be allowed to feed and breed unmolested. All have their natural enemies. As aphid colonies are ravaged by ladybird beetles and aphis lions (see p. fifty-six to fifty-seven), so the larger insects have correspondingly larger and fiercer insect enemies of their own: ground beetles and tiger beetles, mantids and assassin bugs and ant lions. These are well-armed predatory insects. They are the great carnivorous beasts of the insect world, as is indicated by their names. Like the beasts of prey, they pounce upon their victims, or lie in wait for them.

Ground beetles are mostly blackish, flat-bodied insects, that run rapidly, and that keep close to cover. We can find plenty of them in moist places by overturning and looking beneath logs, boards and trash lying on the ground. They feed upon a great variety of the lesser animals that live in such places. The gypsy moth is now in part controlled by the big ground beetle that was imported from Europe for the purpose.

GROUND-BEETLE TIGER-BEETLE

[89]

This beetle was the natural enemy of the moth in its native home in the Old World.

Tiger beetles live in the open. We find them in bare, sunny places by the roadside, and on the exposed sandy shores. Unlike the ground beetles, they take flight readily; and a net will be needed to catch them, and some agility as well. Many of them are beautifully colored. Fresh, clean ones, neatly pinned and mounted, make handsome specimens for the insect collection.

We have already noted that dragonflies are carnivorous and that they chase and capture their prey in flight. So,

A ROBBER-FLY

also, do the big, spiny-legged, t w o - w i n g e d robber-flies. These are able to overpower large and well-armed insects, such as wasps. Robber-flies perch beside our path through the meadow, and dart away ahead of us on our approach; and if we happen to come upon one that has just captured a wasp, we may see a battle royal between them. Fly and wasp fall to the earth together and lie there struggling. The fly with its strong feet holds the wasp's body securely, keeping well out of reach of the sting. At length, if it conquers, it penetrates the wasp's armor with its beak and sucks its blood.

Then there are slow-moving but powerful carnivores like the mantis, that seem to sit still forever, concealed by their own protective coloring, waiting for the prey to wander unwittingly within the reach of the powerful, grasping forelegs. Two joints of the foreleg are hinged to **fold** together closely, and are toothed on their opposed margins to hold securely; and these snap together on their victims like the jaws of a steel trap.

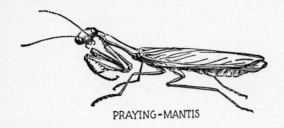

PRAYING-MANTIS

The ant-lion has its own unique way of capturing prey. It digs itself into the sand, and makes a pitfall there, throwing the sand out by upward tosses of its flat head. The funnel-shaped pit so formed has sides as steep as the sand will lie. At the bottom of the pit the ant-lion holds its big, spiny jaws in readiness. When an insect (oftenest an ant), running about over the sand, carelessly steps over the side of the pit, it slides down toward the waiting jaws. If it does not at once slide to the bottom, the ant-lion tosses some more sand into the air to fall on its victim and drive it down within reach.

PIT OF AN ANT-LION

These pits may be found in sheltered, dry, sandy places, and are easily recognized by their uniformity of size, and shape. Their use may be demonstrated by dropping an

[91]

ant into one of them and watching the results. The ant-lion itself may be easily obtained by scooping up a handful of the sand containing it and sifting it out on a piece of window-screen wire cloth. At first it will look like a lump of sand grains stuck together, for the bristling hair that clothes its body holds the sand about it; but soon it will get on its feet and start to run backward.

It may be reared in a dish of dry sand on our table, where it will make new pitfalls every day, as naturally as out of doors. If ants are not at hand, it may be fed on flies. When grown it will cease from feeding, and from making pitfalls, and will spin a spherical white cocoon of silk, down under the sand out of sight, and transform in it into a pupa; and if we keep it a few weeks longer undisturbed, out of the pupa will come a slender, grayish adult insect with long, elegant, gauzy wings.

There are many other insects whose jaws are lengthened and toothed and variously sharpened for use as weapons of defense. Among the true bugs also (Hemiptera), having jointed and puncturing beaks, there are predatory forms. One that attacks us in the night is the bed bug. Often in summer, we may see on a cluster of goldenrod or other flowers a butterfly struggling in the grasp of an ambush bug that has seized it from its place of hiding among the blossoms.

THE WHEEL-BUG

Assassin bugs commonly eat caterpillars. When we see the kind well known in the south as the "wheel-bug" with a cater-

[92]

pillar impaled upon its blood-sucking beak, we recognize a helper in the saving of our crops.

There are three principal groups of pest destroyers that help us in this way. They are: (1) Insect-eating birds and mammals; (2) Predacious insects, like those we have just been considering, and (3) Parasitic insects, that live within or on the bodies of pests, and thus destroy them. The birds we now protect; the others we are just beginning to learn how to use.

Parasites are nature's agents for preventing the undue increase of any species. When any species becomes very abundant, its parasites, finding plenty of food, increase also, and tend to reduce its numbers. Every species has its own parasites. Some of them, like the ichneumon-flies, are large, and live singly, one to a caterpillar; others are

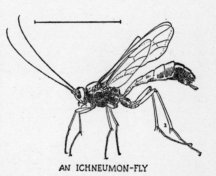

AN ICHNEUMON-FLY

very small and live together in numbers. We are apt to be well impressed with the prevalence of parasites when we first attempt to rear butterflies and moths from their cocoons. Instead of the beautiful insects anticipated, there will often come out a host of these little destroyers, and swarm around on the inside of our rearing cages. On the leaves of plants in the garden, caterpillars are often to be found dead or dying from the attack of these little parasites. Here in our illustration is shown a dead one

[93]

on a leaf of blue grass. The parasites that killed it had come out as full grown larvae through a hole in its skin, and had spun their own cocoons of white silk, some by the side of the caterpillar and others on the leaf above it.

These when dropped into a vial and plugged in with a wad of cotton, hatched out in a few days into the winged adult parasites shown running around on the inside of the vial. This is an easy way by which any one may get to see them. We see little of them in nature; but their work is none the less important; and the control that they exercise is permanent, and natural, and costs us nothing.

BEES, INDOORS AND OUT

The most interesting insect in the world is the honeybee. It is also one of the most abundant and can be studied anywhere. Every one has heard of the industry of the bee in gathering and storing honey, of the skill and mechanical exactness with which it builds its hexagonal cells, of the division of labor within its perfectly organized colony, of the order and system maintained in its household, and of the patriotic zeal with which it defends its home. Yet no one can rightly appreciate these things who has not himself been an eye-witness of them.

The story of the bee is so wonderful it has engaged the attention of good naturalists of all ages; and the books that have been written to tell what they have seen would fill a very large library. We cannot even summarize that story here. The main features of it may be read in many books of natural history, and even in our encyclopedias. But reading alone is not sufficient. We must see and feel in order to know.

The best source of real knowledge of bees will be found in some local apiary. Beekeepers are born naturalists; they must be in order to deal understandingly with their bees; and there is hardly one of them anywhere who will not gladly lend the resources of his apiary for educational use, supplying bees, combs, hives, supers, and other material for study. As a means of actually seeing the bees at work there is nothing equal to an observation hive, perhaps located in the schoolroom window.[1]

Suggested reading. We content ourselves here with a bare outline of a few of the wonderful things to be learned about bees by means of books read at home, helps from the apiary, and observations at the hive.

A. As to the bees themselves.

    I. **Adult bees:** three castes:

        1. A single queen: the mother of the colony; lays all the eggs; has a sting, but uses it only against rival queens; is cared for and fed by workers; rarely seen; to be recognized by her larger size and more graceful form and longer body, the tip of the *pointed* abdomen projecting far beyond the tip of the folded wings.

        2. Drones: males; stingless; present in the colony only during the summer season; killed off by the workers at the end of the season; to be recognized by their stouter bodies, the *blunt* tip of the abdomen hardly projecting beyond the wing tips.

        3. Workers: undeveloped females; each

[1] An observation hive, properly stocked with a small colony of bees ready for the window, and supplied with full instructions as to manner of installation, may be purchased from the A. I. Root Company of Medina, Ohio.

has a sting, and uses it to defend the colony; each has a pollen-basket on outside of the hind leg. To be recognized by smaller size, slender form, and greater activity; also, by vastly greater numbers. Especially worthy of examination with a lens or microscope are:—the sensitive antennae (reversible, to permit entering deep corollas), the nectar-gathering tongue, the hairs of the pollen brushes, above, below, and on legs; the pollen-baskets of the hind legs and the antenna cleaners of the fore legs.

II. **Eggs:** very minute, soft, white; laid by the queen singly in the bottom of the cells of the combs, one in each cell.

III. **Larvae:** soft, white, footless "grubs"; helpless, and fed at frequent intervals until fully grown by "nurse bees" of the worker caste.

IV. **Pupae:** developed within the cells where they have grown up as larvae, after these cells have been capped over by the workers with wax; remaining there to transform; emerging later as adult bees.

B. Bee products.

I. Wax: secreted by wax glands in the bodies of the workers; made from honey that they have previously eaten; moulded by the jaws of the workers into combs, composed of cells that are of remarkable mechanical interest; hexagonal in form, securing utmost economy of material; bases, triangular pyramids, overlapping on the two sides of the comb, giving maximum strength. Cells of three sorts: two, ordinary horizontal cells; one special, vertical cell.

    1. Worker cells: smaller; the most common type.

    2. Drone cells: larger and often nearer the edge of the comb; also used for honey storage.

    3. Queen cells: made preparatory to swarming, and present only when queens are to be reared; usually pendant on the lower margin of the combs: very large, and conspicuous.

  II. *Honey:* gathered as nectar from flowers, and ripened.

  III. *Propolis:* a gummy substance gathered from buds of trees and used by the bees for stopping cracks.

  IV. *"Bee-bread":* made from honey and pollen, and used for larval food.

  V. *"Royal jelly":* a special food for queen larvae.

C. Bee dwellings.

  I. The original home of bees: a hollow tree.

  II. Artificial hives, that we have substituted.

Skeps, and "gums" (sections of hollow
log).

Box hives with movable combs.

Brood combs for permanent occupancy and
for brood-rearing.

Supers, for honey storage.

D. Activities of the colony.

    I. Brood-rearing, queen rearing, drone rearing,
and swarming.

   II. Cleaning and ventilation of the hive.

  III. Storage of "bee-bread" and evaporation of
surplus water from honey.

  IV. Ventilation of the hive by fanning with the
wings for temperature control.

Field observations. There are some things we can do
with bees without asking aid from anybody. We can observe their field activities. No less wonderful is the work
of the bees out of doors.

These vast stores of honey, that were for ages the chief
source of sweets for human kind—whence do they come?
How long would it take us to gather a teaspoonful of the
nectar of flowers and how would we go about it?

Suppose we follow a bee that is gathering nectar from
the flowers of goldenrods or asters and see how she does
it. She plumps down upon a flower cluster, unslings her
doubled-up tongue, and quickly dips the tip of it into a
single corolla. Before we can see what is going on she
has it out again, and dips it into another, and another, and
another; and then, with a flash of wings, she is away to
another cluster.

[99]

Let us find the nectar. We pluck off a head, and separate out from it a single trumpet-shaped flower. We look down into its minute opening and can see nothing there. We split the corolla open down one side with a pin point, and use a lens, and there, just above the base of a stamen, where the corolla widens, is a shining droplet of nectar—hardly enough to see, and not at all enough to taste, with our dull tongues.

We may find more nectar in a fresh head of red clover, and we may taste it by plucking a few corollas from the head and pressing their bases between our lips. The closed corollas of red clover are so deep that the honeybee cannot reach the bottom: its tongue is not long enough. But it is able to glean where stores are very scanty in other shallower flowers.

The honeybee gathers its stores with infinite labor. The load of nectar that it carries home is gathered from many flowers. We may gain some idea of how many if we count the number of corollas that it probes in one minute, and then bear in mind that each trip from the hive requires from 15 to 90 minutes. Here is a splendid illustration of the old Scotch proverb "Mony mickles mak a muckle"! or of our own American version: "Every little bit, added to what she's got, makes the bee just a little bit more."

The bee gathers pollen also, and mixes it with honey to make "bee-bread" for food. She is provided with branching bristly hairs above and below and on her legs. The pollen sticks to these hairs. With the spines of her legs she combs these hairs, taking up the pollen and depositing it in the "pollen-baskets" on the outside of her hind legs. When she has filled her pollen-baskets they are quite conspicuous.

In the economy of nature, a wonderful service to the plant world is rendered by the bee unwittingly while she is gathering pollen. Some of it is lost in the gatherings; and some of it is left on the stigmas of the flowers visited, to grow there, to fertilize the flowers and to cause them to produce seed. The hum of the bees among the cherry and apple blossoms is a necessary forerunner to the development of a crop of fruit.

In most flowers the anther that produces the pollen and the stigma that receives it are so placed that they are rubbed in succession by the same part of the bee's body. In flowers like goldenrod and aster they are rubbed by the hairs on the under parts; in the two-lipped flowers of the mints they are placed together overhead, under an overarching upper lip where they are rubbed by the hairs on the back. This is a part of the Fitness of Things.

The bees are Nature's chief animal agents for the distribution of pollen. Other insects do it, but not so efficiently; butterflies and syrphus flies and beetles. Whether we watch them working on the asters in autumn or on the apple blossoms in spring, we shall see that beetles are slow and lumbering, and that butterflies and syrphus flies, though quick, are wary and loitering; and it is only the bees that proceed in a business-like manner, working rapidly and steadily and effectively. The bees have developed a household economy based on pollen and nectar. The wonderful efficiency of the bee in the field goes along with the organized life in the hive.

THE CONTROL OF INSECT PESTS

The first requisite for control of insect pests is knowledge of their habits and life histories. Without this there can be no intelligent application of a remedy. A vast store of such knowledge is available in government publications, and these are available to all who need them.

There are four principal kinds of control that we may exercise over injurious insects:

1. Control by insecticides, mainly poisons.
2. Control by traps:—fly traps; roach traps; trap lanterns; tanglefoot.
3. Control by cultural methods:—planting early for the cotton boll weevil; planting late for the pea weevil; plowing in the fall for wireworms; mowing the crop early for clover seed insects; destroying fallen stalks for the European corn borer. These methods demand accurate knowledge of times and seasons and habits.
4. Control by natural enemies:—predacious enemies such as lady-bird beetles; insectivorous birds; skunks, etc.; parasitic enemies such as ichneumon flies, tachina flies, chalcis flies, etc. This is nature's method. It is the only permanent control.

Control by insecticides is the method usually chosen for quick results.

Something about insecticides. We have seen (pages twenty-one and forty-one and forty-two) how different are biting and sucking insects in their manner of feeding. This difference underlies our selection of insecticides for control. There are two kinds of poisons; one kind for

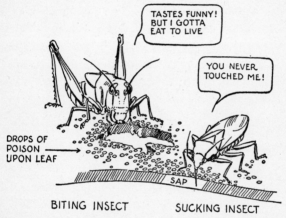

DROPS OF
POISON
UPON LEAF

TASTES FUNNY!
BUT I GOTTA
EAT TO LIVE

YOU NEVER
TOUCHED ME!

SAP

BITING INSECT   SUCKING INSECT

biting and one for sucking insects. Accordingly they fall into these two groups:

1. **Food poisons.** These are for biting insects. They are applied to the food, usually in the form of a dust or a spray. They are eaten along with the food, and take effect when absorbed in the stomach of the insect. The food poisons are mainly arsenicals. Paris green is effective and cheap and quick-acting, but it has a tendency to "burn" tender foliage. Arsenate of lead is less harmful to green leaves, and somewhat slower in action, but stays on the leaves and is effective for a longer time.

2. **Contact poisons.** These are for sucking insects. These are applied to the bodies of the pests, either as a spray or as a dust or as a gas. They kill by contact. Cyanide gas is one of them. In the citrus groves of Florida and California this gas is put in big gas-proof tents placed over single trees. It enters the spiracles of the insects and quickly kills them. This is an expensive method, that is applicable only to very valuable crops. It is this same gas that kills the insects in your cyanide bottle. There it is slowly given off from the potassium cyanide stored in the bottle. Calcium cyanide is another common source of it. This, when used as dust or as thin flakes, gives off the gas slowly when in contact with moisture-laden air, as in a greenhouse, where it may be used (with extreme caution) to kill scale insects and aphids.

A widely used contact insecticide is nicotine sulfate (one common brand of which is known as "Black Leaf 40"). This in dilute solution gives off fumes effectively, in quantities that are not dangerous for us to use. This is one of the best insecticides for aphids out of doors.

Carbon bisulphide is a heavy liquid that gives off poisonous fumes, and that is much used for fumigating in closed containers, such as bins, closets and chests. The gas is heavy and settles. If evaporated from a dish set upon the top of a pile of grain in a bin, it will penetrate downward through the pile and kill not only the grain insects, but mice and rats as well. The gas is highly explosive and no fire, not even a lighted cigar, may be allowed near it.

There are a few standard insecticides that meet most

of our needs, but there is no single one that is best for all injurious species. We learn from the use of our cyanide bottle that some insects are much harder to kill than others. Bees and flies and other very active insects are killed almost at once when shut inside it, while some of the heavier and more sluggish beetles withstand its fumes better, and remain active for some time. The standard nicotine spray will quickly kill apple red bugs while they are young and thin-skinned; but it is rather ineffective against the adults.

Food poisons are best and cheapest for insects that will eat them; but, being applied to the surface, they are obviously useless for killing those other insects that get their food entirely from beneath the surface. The latter are reached by other means.

Para-dichloro-benzine (which may be asked for at your drug store as PDB) is a slower acting insect poison that is not poisonous to man. It comes in white crystals that evaporate slowly, producing a gas that is effective against clothes moths if hung in a cheese-cloth bag in the top of your clothes-press; also, against museum pests, if kept in a tray in your insect cases.

There are three principal ways of applying insecticides: spraying, dusting, and mixing with bait. Ingenious sprayers and dusters have been devised for their application. We may learn of these from advertisement in the farm and garden periodicals. The beginner can do no better than to buy standard insecticide preparations and follow the directions that are printed on the packages. But for his small troubles with insects of the household or of the home garden very simple apparatus will suffice. The aphids on the tip of the new apple plantling, for example, or those on the potted window geranium, may be dipped into a pail of nicotine sulfate solution; or the potato beetles on a few rows in the garden may have Paris green dusted on them from a pepper box or a cheese-cloth bag.

It must always be remembered that apparatus will avail little unless the cause of the trouble and the action of the remedy are first understood.

HOW TO BEGIN AN INSECT COLLECTION

A good way to begin the study of insects is by making a small collection of them. In order to get specimens for study the first thing needed is a good killing bottle, such as a cyanide bottle; one that will kill them quickly, so that specimens may be obtained undamaged and in good condition for display in your collection.

A cyanide bottle is a wide-mouthed bottle of clear glass containing cyanide of potassium. This substance gives

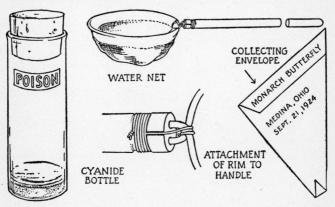

POISON

WATER NET

COLLECTING
ENVELOPE

MONARCH BUTTERFLY

MEDINA, OHIO
SEPT. 21, 1924

CYANIDE
BOTTLE

ATTACHMENT
OF RIM TO
HANDLE

off poisonous fumes by which insects, when shut inside the bottle, are quickly and quietly killed. The cyanide is most conveniently used in powdered form; and if a little powdered boracic acid be mixed with it, the fumes will be given off more rapidly, and the bottle will be stronger and more effective. The poison is held in the bottom of the bottle under tight-fitting discs of porous pith or of heavy blotting paper, glued to the glass at the edges. The fumes of cyanide are not very dangerous to us (a whiff will do no harm), but the cyanide is very poisonous if taken internally, and every cyanide bottle should bear a **POISON** label.

Many a good capture may be made with a cyanide bottle alone; for stray insects, often beautiful ones, will sometimes fly in at an open window, and stop, baffled, bumping against the window pane, vainly trying to get out again; and it is easy to place the open mouth of the cyanide bottle over them, and capture them there. Pretty moths and beetles come to the porch lights on warm evenings, and when they settle on the pillars and ceiling the ever-useful cyanide bottle will take them. On the flowers of the garden brilliant bees and flies will be found resting, and these, if approached cautiously, may be brushed into the bottle held in one hand by means of the cork held in the other.

For collecting the more fleet and wary insects, a net will be needed. The larger butterflies and dragonflies will be hard enough to capture even with a net. **The standard insect collecting net** is 12 inches in diameter of rim with a handle about 3 feet long. To facilitate getting out the catch, the bag should taper to the bottom, and it should not be deeper than the length of the arm of the person using it: 18 or 20 inches is deep enough. The bag is made of some kind of netting, with a top-band of muslin. A light strong net is best.

The use of an insect net is very simple. When, by a

quick stroke, an insect has been swept into it, a turn of the wrist makes a fold in the bag of the net, keeping the insect in its bottom. Then an open cyanide bottle is pushed up into the net, and carefully placed over the confined insect. Then the cork is inserted—at first, more safely from outside the net, if there be a stinging insect, like a wasp, inside it. Skill in using both net and bottle will come with a little practice.

A water net for collecting aquatic insects must be much more stoutly built, smaller in diameter, if of fine mesh, and shallow, its depth not exceeding its diameter. One may be made as shown in the last figure if a piece of heavy fence wire and a broom-stick or a similar handle be at hand. For a rim, the wire is bent in a circle, with ends crossed and bent parallel. These parallel ends are inserted in two small holes bored in the end of the handle. To keep the net from coming off the handle a piece of small wire is wrapped across the ends of the rim and then drawn tightly down into grooves cut in the handle as indicated in the figure, wrapped and twisted and hammered down flat. The net is then sewed to the rim.

A heavy beating net for collecting insects from foliage, and having the dimensions of the standard net first described above may be home-made after this manner also.

Paper envelopes, such as professional entomologists use, for temporary storage of the larger insects that are not to be at once pinned, are made as needed out of rectangles of white paper. A piece, say post-card size or about 3 × 5 inches, is folded diagonally across the middle, as shown in the illustration. One overlapping end is folded across the edge, and is crimped by means of a cross fold of its tip. This makes the container, into which the insect, with wings folded over its back, is placed after it is dead. Then the other projecting flap is similarly folded over and crimped to close the envelope. Name, date and locality are written upon the outside. Specimens so papered may be kept until needed in any tight (pest proof) box. They require little space and furnish good material for study in winter. If kept in cigar boxes which are generally not pest-proof, a little cloth bag containing a tablespoon of crystals of PDB (the trade designation of para-dichloro-benzine) should be kept in each box with the specimens; and the PDB should be renewed each month, or as often as the crystals are entirely evaporated. PDB is not poisonous to humans, but it acts too slowly for use in killing bottles.

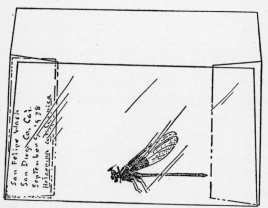

Cellophane envelopes are excellent permanent containers for the specimens. They are inexpensive, occupy little space and save much time in study. Without removal from the envelopes the insects may be examined from both sides. They may be handled with much less breakage than pinned specimens, and if breaks occur the parts are not scattered around in a box, but are retained in the envelope. The standard size is $4\frac{1}{8} \times 2\frac{1}{4}$ inches with a flap $\frac{3}{4}$ inch wide at the top.

They may be filed in their trays like cards in a drawer. The tops should be left open for easy removal of the specimen whenever removal is necessary. The free flap facilitates handling.

Insect pins are of standard length and form, and no other pins are suitable; numbers 1, 2, and 3 are the most generally useful. Usually insect collections are still kept on pins.

Most insects should have the pin run vertically through the middle of the body. For uniformity in appearance one-fourth inch of its length should be above the back of the specimen. There are depth gauges, but it takes time to use them; and you may use your finger instead, by grasping the pinhead uniformly, and pushing the pinpoint downward through the insect until your finger-tip touches its back. Most beetles are pinned through the right wing cover (see p. forty-seven) ; very small ones are glued to paper points and these points are pinned (see p. sixty-six) ; midges and very small flies are mounted on pin points (see p. fifty-nine). All should stand at uniform height and legs and antennae should be arranged in natural positions.

Spreading boards are of two principal sorts. Both of them are used to prepare specimens for display with wings fully expanded. The simpler sort is merely a smooth soft-wood board having a row of pin holes a quarter of an inch deep down the middle of it. On this board the insect to be spread is placed up-side down, with the head end of the pin on which it is impaled thrust down loosely into the bottom of one of the holes. Legs and antennae are more easily arranged on this type of board.

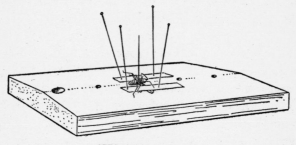

SPREADING BOARD

The other sort of board has the top in two long strips, and the insect is pinned in an erect position with its body down in the space between the strips, its wings upon their upper surface extended flat, and held in position under strips of paper pinned across them until dry. The fore wings are drawn forward until their hind margins are in a straight line across the axis of the body, and the hind wings are drawn forward to meet the front ones properly. Both boards when properly constructed have the surface sloped so as to give the wings a little upward slant—this to allow for a little natural drooping after removal to the display case. Grasshoppers are usually prepared for the cabinet by spreading the wings of one side only; flies, beetles and bugs, with no spreading of the wings at all.

The latter type of board is best for insects having on the back tufts of scales or of hairs that should not be depressed.

Proper spreading of the wings of little moths is something of an art. Nothing will make or mar the appearance of the showier insects more than the spread of their wings. They must be symmetrically placed. A hooked pin point is often useful in drawing them into position. The fine colors of the wings of butterflies and moths are in the scales, and these must not be rubbed off.

A drying box with shelves upon which spreading boards may be placed, and with ventilating windows covered with fine meshed wire cloth to keep out museum pests, is a convenience that any handy man can provide. Spread specimens must be left on the boards until thoroughly dry (a week, perhaps), for if removed too soon, the wings will droop.

A moistening, or relaxing jar, is usually a glazed earthenware 2-gallon jar containing a layer of moist sand in the bottom covered by clean paper, and closed with a lid. Any kind of moist chamber will answer the purpose. Papered specimens placed inside it for 24 hours become relaxed and flexible again, and may then be pinned and mounted on a spreading board, almost as when fresh.

Alcohol for preserving insects should be of 70 per cent to 80 per cent strength. Ninety-five per cent alcohol ("proof spirit") hardens too much, and makes the specimens brittle. Formalin is not recommended for insects. Soft-bodied insects, and the immature stages of all insects are usually preserved in vials.

Neatness in the arrangement of the specimens in parallel rows and with uniform spacing has much to do with the good appearance of a collection: so, also, has neatness and uniformity of labeling. Lastly, **dry specimens can only be kept permanently in pest proof containers.**

HOW TO REAR INSECTS

Much may be learned about the life histories of insects with very simple equipment. We have already seen (page seventy-two) that mosquitos may be reared from the egg through all their transformations in a dish of water on

REARING CAGE

our table; and that cabbage worms (page twenty-one) may be reared to butterflies in a fruit jar or in a jelly tumbler with a lid.

Grasshoppers and other insects that feed on grasses you may keep under observation in this way: Plant a grass sod in a large flower pot. Cover the sod with a lantern globe or other large glass cylinder, and press its lower end down into the soil of the pot. Cover the top of the cylinder with a piece of cheese cloth or other netting, held in place with a rubber band or tied on with a string. Then put the grasshoppers inside.

Dragonfly larvae, water beetles, and other pond insects may be kept under observation in any small aquarium— even in any glass jar of pond water.[1] Adult dragonflies

[1] Heavily chlorinated water from city water mains may kill them. Get rainwater, or water from a clean pond or stream.

[114]

may be reared in the pillow cage shown in the accompanying figure. You may easily make this cage from an 18-inch square piece of ordinary window-screen wire cloth. Bring two opposite margins of the piece together, flat wise, and over-fold them together twice in a "tinker's hem." Flatten down the seam, by hammering or by stepping on it when laid on the floor. Then with one hand placed inside, expand it into a cylinder, with a seam down one side. Then flatten and in similar manner twice cross fold one end for a bottom, and again expand by spreading with

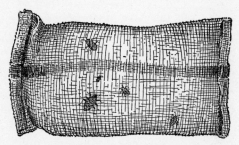

SCREEN CAGE FOR REARING INSECTS

the hands at the new hem. Now it is ready to receive the living specimens. Set it in an aquarium or in a pail of pond water, put in the dragonfly larvae and close the top by a single cross fold. This top fold may be opened and closed with the finger for putting in food or taking out specimens. The cage should stand or should be hung in a slanting position with three-fourths of its length above the water, in order to allow to any adult dragonflies that may emerge space for expanding and drying their wings.

The easiest way to rear most kinds of common insect larvae, if they are found near at hand, is to let them rear

[115]

themselves until they are almost ready to transform. Look in on them frequently, and take them indoors only at the end of the larval period when feeding is over. This means for most insects collecting and rearing the pupae; but grasshoppers, bugs and dragonflies have no pupal stage. Pupae require no food, and need only to be kept under suitable living conditions in order to obtain the adult insects from them.

There is one rule above all others that leads to success in rearing insects: **Provide natural conditions**: imitate in so far as possible the conditions under which you find them thriving in nature.

Losses will occur in rearing pupae: deaths from evaporation due to keeping them in too dry a place; deaths from overgrowth of moulds due to keeping them in too wet a place. If pupae are kept in a glass jar indoors, a wet sponge may be hung inside the jar to keep moisture in the air, and a fine meshed netting may be kept over the open top to allow a circulation of the air that will prevent excess of moisture. The netting will also retain any minute parasites that may hatch from the pupae, and that, without it, might escape unnoticed.

SUGGESTIONS FOR THE USE OF THIS BOOK

Study living insects first if possible, for they are much more interesting than dead specimens; and only with living things may transformations and other activities be observed. Although your first interest may be in what they are called, what they are like, what they can do, and what they are good for, there are yet a few things that you should learn early about their structure and development; for you need to know the parts of their bodies and the manner of their growing up in order to talk intelligently about them. Grasshoppers and butterflies and beetles are everywhere available. The out-door world is full of excellent illustrative material. Get it and use it freely.

Some ABC's of Insect Study

An insect differs from the larger animals that are more familiar to us in having no bones in its body. It wears its skeleton as a hard shell on the outside. There are three main divisions in its body, as shown here in our diagram: HEAD, THORAX and ABDOMEN.

The **head** goes foremost. To it belong the mouthparts (lips and jaws) and sense organs (eyes and antennae), and this is how to find them:

The mouth is at the lower side of the head. It is surrounded by parts that may easily be seen by looking at the

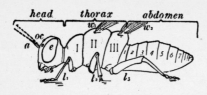

head of a grasshopper or a dragonfly or a beetle. By poking the lips aside with a pin point two pairs of jaws may be found lying between them. These jaws do not move up and down like ours, but they swing from side to side, meeting on the middle line by more or less jagged teeth. These parts may be identified as follows:

1. An upper lip, a simple flap of membrane hanging down from above.
2. A lower lip, two lobed, and with a pair of little feelers (palps) on it, one feeler sticking out on each side.
3. A pair of stout horny jaws (*mandibles*) beneath the upper lip.
4. A pair of slenderer but more complicated second jaws (maxillae) next to the lower lip. These also bear a pair of little food feelers, one on each, at the side.

The jaws may be pried apart with a pin point to expose the mouth between them.

If this seems a queer sort of a mouth as compared with our own, the other parts of the head are still more queer,—or at least more different. The sense organs of the head are of two sorts: eyes and antennae; these may be identified as follows:

[118]

1. Large compound eyes at the sides of the head. These are made up of a multitude of little windows (facets) of microscopic size (just about big enough to be seen with a pocket lens); each facet has its own lens, and focuses its own beams of light. The points of light from all the little windows together make on the inside a picture of the things appearing in the world outside. This sort of an eye is believed to be especially good for seeing moving objects.

2. Little eyes called ocelli, not always present, but when present generally three in number, placed in a triangle, the foremost one in the middle line of the top of the head or face. Though very small they may easily be found on the head of a grasshopper or dragonfly.

3. Antennae or feelers. These project forward from the front of the head somewhere between the eyes. They are very large and conspicuous in grasshoppers and beetles; slender and bristle-like in dragonflies, and very different in form in other insects, but in all they are made up of a series of joints, and bear sense organs. We have no comparable parts, and so have some difficulty in knowing what impressions of the outside world they bring to their possessors.

The **thorax** is divided into three segments (I, II, and III of the accompanying diagram), each of which has a leg attached to it below, and the second and third of which may each bear a pair of wings. Each leg is made up of a series of joints, with two little joints at the base making the upturn from the body, two long joints meeting at the knee, and a few more little joints making the foot. The last joint of the foot generally bears a pair of claws. All these joints are easily flexed in fresh specimens[1] to see how they work.

The wings are usually thin, transparent membranes stretched over a supporting framework of veins. However in the beetles the fore wings are hard horny sheaths that completely cover the body to rearward, and only the hind wings are thin and membranous. Underneath the fore wings the hind ones are folded very compactly when at rest. By lifting a fore wing and pulling a hind wing forward by its front margin the latter will unfold amazingly, both lengthwise and crosswise, as it has to do when the beetle is taking flight. The fore wings of beetles serve only for protection.

Now a little about the way in which insects grow up. They all hatch from eggs, and are at first very small and soft and pale. Each little infant when first released from the cramped quarters of the egg shell, stretches itself and expands and becomes darker in color as its skin hardens on exposure to the air. Then it begins to feed and grow, and of course, its tough armor-like skin when once hardened will not stretch very much. It soon becomes too small. It has to be cast off and replaced by a new and larger one, like a small boy's outgrown shirt.

This is the way it gets a new one: When the old tough outer skin gets too tight it becomes loosened from the soft underlying skin, and then, with pressure from within, it splits lengthwise down the back of the head and thorax. Out of the split the soft body squeezes its way, head and thorax first, legs and abdomen following. This is what is

[1] Dried insects may be instantly made flexible again by a dip into boiling water.

called molting. After each molt an expansion and increase in stature occurs at once while the skin is new and still stretchable. Then it hardens and darkens again and the insect goes on feeding until another molt becomes necessary to accommodate additional growth. All this may be readily seen without very long waiting in a cage of young grasshoppers kept supplied with clover leaves, or in an aquarium of young dragonflies that have been given mosquito wrigglers to eat.

The number of molts after hatching is different in different kinds of insects. In the examples shown in the two next following figures it is five. In dragonflies it is about a dozen. In most weevils it is only three.

It will be seen that there is increase in size but very little change in form at each of these regular moltings; but when full size has been attained, then there occurs a change of form[1] that is truly wonderful, that is peculiar to insects, and that every one should know about.

In different insects this vast change comes about in two ways. The transformation may be either:

Incomplete, with three stages { Egg / Larva or / Adult

Complete, with four stages { Egg / Larva / Pupa / Adult

In both, growth and regular moltings continue through the larval stage, and the great change of form comes at

[1] Called from the Latin, *transformation;* from the Greek, *metamorphosis.*

its close. The presence or absence of a pupal stage distinguishes the two.

Correspondingly, there are two general types of larvae. In the first group the larvae[2] have much the same form as the adult. They are generally so like the adult as to be easily recognized as its young, as in the plant bug whose life history is pictured herewith. A young grasshopper is plainly a grasshopper; but a caterpillar is very different from a butterfly. It will be noticed on carefully looking at the small figures of the plant bug that the wing buds appear on the back of the larvae after its second molt, and that they increase in size with each of the third and fourth molts. They expand at the last molt into the large wings of the adult, and are the most marked feature of its final transformation.

In the second group the larvae[3] are very different from the adults. They are often more or less worm-like in form.[4] No wings appear on the back. Legs and antennae are greatly reduced in size (or may be altogether wanting in fly larvae), and the abdomen is greatly enlarged. This larva is so very different that a special period for making it over into the adult form is needed, and hence the pupal

[2] Larva is a general term for the first form taken on by many animals, for example, a tadpole is a frog larva. The name **nymph** is commonly applied to larvae of this first group.

[3] This kind of larvae is called by a great variety of common names, such as **caterpillars** in moths and butterflies, **maggots** in two-winged flies, **grubs** in beetles, etc.

[4] Wherefore, some moth larvae are known as **cut worms,** others as **span worms,** others as **horn worms;** certain beetle larvae as **wire worms,** etc. Of course, they are not true worms at all. Common names are often founded on very slight resemblances.

[122]

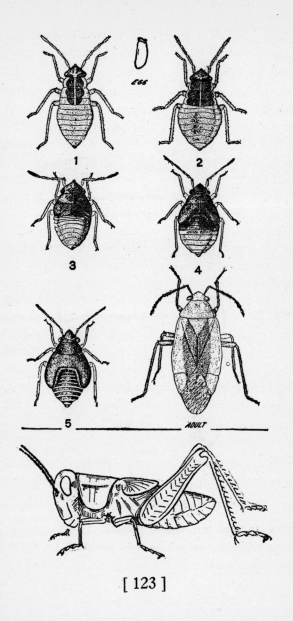

EGG

1

2

3

4

5   ADULT

period. This is a period of inactivity, spent in some sheltered place of retirement, while the making-over processes are going on.

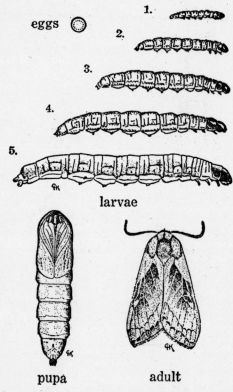

eggs

1.

2.

3.

4.

5.

larvae

pupa   adult

This is the high point and culmination of one of the most remarkable phenomena of the animal world.

How to find out about insects: If there be a good library available, you may help yourself by the use of books—especially, well-illustrated books. Most of our injurious insects, and many other insects, are figured in a number of reference books of entomology, such as the following:

COMSTOCK, J. H., *Introduction to Entomology*
COMSTOCK, MRS. J. H., *A Handbook of Nature Study*
CROSBY AND LEONARD, *A Manual of Garden Insects*
ESSIG, E. O., *Insects of Western North America*
LUTZ, F., *A Field Book of Insects*
HERRICK, G. W., *Household Insects*
METCALF AND FLINT, *Destructive and Useful Insects*
NEEDHAM, J. G., *Elementary Lessons on Insects*
ROOT, A. I., *The A. B. C. and X. Y. Z. of Bee Culture*
SINGERLAND AND CROSBY, *A Manual of Fruit Insects*

Often there is a local entomologist who will take pleasure in naming insects for a beginner; and usually he will know to whom to send them if he cannot name them himself. If specimens are to be shipped to some specialist they must arrive in fit condition for study. It will not do to merely enclose them in a letter; for if so sent, they may arrive at his office in the form of an unrecognizable smear. Larvae and soft-bodied insects may be put in vials of alcohol (70 per cent to 80 per cent strength), packed in a box with plenty of soft wrapping to protect them from breakage, and sent as fourth class mail. The cylindrical mailing cases of pasteboard with metal caps, now in general use, are good containers. Most adult insects are best sent in paper envelopes (see p. ninety-one) packed lightly in a stout box. Information as to where they are found (on what plants, etc.) and what damage they were doing should be supplied with the specimens.

By such means as are presented in the preceding pages any one may get acquainted with insects. The means are within the reach of all, and insects are everywhere available in great variety.

Collection-making has been among the early interests of many a great naturalist. Observation of the ways of insects is a source of pleasure to very many people who love Nature, and who find delight in personal knowledge of her infinite resources.

INDEX

[128]